Contracts for Independent Readers

Humor

Grades 4–6

Writers:
Jan Brennan and Mary Sanford

Editors:
Kim T. Griswell and Cayce Guiliano

Contributing Editors:
Cindy K. Daoust and Mary Lester

Art Coordinator:
Donna K. Teal

Artists:
Nick Greenwood, Clevell Harris, Sheila Krill, Mary Lester,
Rebecca Saunders, Barry Slate, Donna K. Teal

Cover Artist:
Nick Greenwood

www.themailbox.com

©2001 by THE EDUCATION CENTER, INC.
All rights reserved.
ISBN #1-56234-404-8

Manufactured in the United States

10 9 8 7 6 5 4 3 2 1

Table of Contents

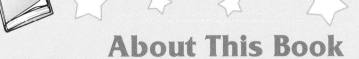

About This Book

What is humor?

Humorous literature is literature that the reader finds funny. Humor can be incorporated into a novel using devices such as mimicry, slapstick, buffoonery, farce, hyperbole, parody, ridicule, cartoon, nonsense, puns, conundrums, and idioms. Humorous books can relieve anxiety, entice a reluctant reader, and lighten the atmosphere.

How to use this book:

Contracts for Independent Readers—Humor includes everything you will need to implement an independent reading program in your classroom.

The **Teacher's Organizational Checklist** on page 4 will help you monitor your students' progress throughout the year. To use this page, photocopy it to make a class supply and write each student's name in the space provided. Hold a conference with each student to assess the goals the student has for the semester or the year. Have the student write her goals in the space provided. Next, have each student choose one of the novels included in this book to read. List the title of the book in the appropriate column. When the student has completed an activity, write the date it was completed in the bottom portion of the corresponding box. Use the key at the bottom of the page to note the type of activity completed in the top portion of the corresponding box as shown in the sample. After evaluating the activities, write any comments you have in the space provided and have the student do the same. At the end of the semester or year, direct each student to complete the self-assessment portion detailing how she feels she has done at reaching her goals. Finally, write your own assessment of each student's progress.

The **introductory page** of each independent contract contains a description of the novel, background information on the author, and a student contract materials list. This list will aid you in preparing in advance any materials that students may need. Most of the listed materials can be found right in the classroom!

Each of the two programmable **contract pages** in each unit has six independent activities for students to choose from. Each unit also includes **reproducible pages** that correspond to several independent activities. The second contract page has slightly more advanced activities than the first contract page.

Since some novels are at higher reading levels or may contain more mature content, we suggest that you read each of the novels so that you may assist students in choosing which novels to read.

Also included in this book is a **student booklist** on page 61, which consists of 12 humorous novels, with a brief description of each. This list provides you with additional titles for students who finish early, for students who would enjoy reading other books in this genre, and for you to include in your classroom library.

Other Books in the Contracts for Independent Readers Series:
- *Contracts for Independent Readers—Historical Fiction*
- *Contracts for Independent Readers—Realistic Fiction*
- *Contracts for Independent Readers—Fantasy*
- *Contracts for Independent Readers—Adventure*
- *Contracts for Independent Readers—Mystery*

Name _____

4

Book Title	Activity 1	Activity 2	Activity 3	Activity 4	Activity 5	Activity 6	Activity 7	Activity 8	Activity 9	Activity 10	Activity 11	Activity 12	Teacher Comments	Student Comments
Sample: Book Title	MA 11/6	SS 11/7		LA 11/10										

Student Goals:

Self-Assessment:

Teacher Assessment:

Key

LA = Language Arts
RD = Reading
W = Writing
MA = Math
SS = Social Studies
SC = Science
A = Art
MU = Music
RS = Research
CT = Critical Thinking

Be a Perfect Person in Just Three Days!

by Stephen Manes

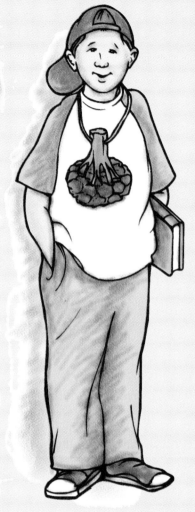

About the Book

Milo Crinkley wants to be perfect. He is tired of the clumsy accidents that always happen to him. When the book *Be a Perfect Person in Just Three Days!* falls off a library shelf and hits Milo on the head, he decides to give it a try. On each of three days, Milo has to carry out an assignment and learn an important lesson. After day one, Milo learns that he has courage. After day two, he learns that he has willpower. After day three, Milo learns that being a good person is much better and much more fun than being perfect. After making it through the three days, Milo discovers that there is no such thing as a perfect person, but maybe that's not so bad after all!

About the Author

Stephen Manes was born on January 8, 1949, in Pittsburgh, Pennsylvania. Stephen began his writing career in the third grade when he was a reporter for his school newspaper. Later, in middle school he won several honors for humorous and satirical pieces he had entered in statewide competitions.

Manes also loved photography and decided to combine his two loves into a career. He moved out to Hollywood to try his hand at becoming a movie director, but soon realized that Hollywood was not the place for him. Manes and his first wife, Esther, a children's  librarian, moved back East, where he tried writing children's books. In very little time he had earned a reputation for his fun and out-of-the-ordinary characters. While the serious side of him writes nonfiction books and magazine columns about computers, the spunky side writes for kids. Manes feels a need to nurture the sense of silliness that children have and all too often lose by adulthood.

Student Contract Materials List

- Activity #1: copy of page 8
- Activity #2: white construction paper, scissors
- Activity #3: white drawing paper, crayons or markers
- Activity #4: white drawing paper, crayons or markers
- Activity #5: construction paper, crayons or markers
- Activity #6: paper, pencil
- Activity #7: paper, pencil
- Activity #8: paper, pencil
- Activity #9: white drawing paper, crayons or markers
- Activity #10: white drawing paper, crayons or markers
- Activity #11: copy of page 9
- Activity #12: copy of page 10, 1 sheet of 8½" x 11" tagboard, 10 index cards, 2 game pieces

Be a Perfect Person in Just Three Days!

Independent Contract

Name:_____ Number of activities to be completed: _____

1. Science

On day two of Dr. Silverfish's plan to become a perfect person, Milo can't eat or drink anything except water. When the 24 hours are up, Milo eats an incredible amount of food. Does Milo choose nutritious foods? Would you have chosen nutritious foods? Obtain a copy of page 8 from your teacher to learn more about nutritious food choices.

2. Writing

Milo has two dreams about being perfect. In the first dream, in chapter 2, he laughs at all the imperfect people he sees below him. In the second dream, in chapter 5, he gets a more somber, boring view of perfection. Reread these two dreams; then close your eyes and daydream about being perfect. What is it like? Draw a cloud shape and cut it out. On the back of the cloud write about your daydream of being perfect.

3. Art

In chapter 1, Milo describes what Dr. K. Pinkerton Silverfish looks like in his picture on the back of the book. After seeing the picture, Milo seriously doubts the doctor's credentials for teaching anyone how to be perfect. Reread this section of chapter 1 and then draw a portrait of Dr. K. Pinkerton Silverfish based on Milo's description. Include a frame and a short caption telling who the doctor is.

4. Math

Before Milo begins his three-day journey to perfection, he grabs a snack of two Creme-Stuft Twinkles and a glass of milk, then goes to do his homework. How perfect a snack is that? Plan four "perfect snacks" and then draw a picture of each one. Survey your classmates to find out which of the four snacks they feel is the most perfect. Create a bar graph or pictograph showing the results of your survey.

5. Language Arts

From the National Geography Bee to the National Basketball Association Championship, people earn awards in our country all the time. When Milo fasts for an entire day he proves he has stick-to-it-iveness, or willpower, one essential ingredient of perfection. Design four original awards you can present to different family members or friends who have demonstrated exceptional willpower. On the back of each award, write a paragraph explaining how each person has earned it.

6. Writing

In chapter 2, Milo goes into the living room to ask his mom if he may take some broccoli from the refrigerator. He finds his parents watching the news on television. They are so interested in the news story about the gorilla war at the zoo that he is not sure they have heard what he has asked them. Pretend you are an eyewitness to this gorilla war at the zoo. Write a lively report about what you've seen.

Be a Perfect Person in Just Three Days!

Independent Contract

Name:_____ Number of activities to be completed: _____

7. Language Arts

Milo believes that if he can become a perfect person, all of his problems will be solved. Unfortunately, when he completes the program he is still not perfect. What he learns is that being a perfect person is very boring. Milo decides that it would be better to be a good person. Write two *acrostic poems,* or poems that use the letters of a word or words to begin each line. Use "PERFECT PERSON" for one poem and "GOOD PERSON" for the other poem.

8. Writing

For three days, Milo carefully follows Dr. Silverfish's instructions, even though they are bizarre. Imagine what Milo would record if he kept a journal while he was working at becoming perfect. Write a journal entry for each day, from Milo's point of view. Include what he thinks about the plan, what others say, how he feels, and anything else you think he might want to write down.

9. Social Studies

Everyone has some idea of what a perfect person would or would not do. Interview several people to find out what things they think a perfect person would never do. Make a pamphlet including the ten best ideas and title it "The 10 Things a Perfect Person Would Never Do." Then illustrate each tip.

10. Art

The first step Milo has to take to perfection is wearing a stalk of broccoli around his neck. This single item draws a great deal of attention. Reread chapter 3 to review the clever explanations Milo gives as to why he is wearing broccoli. What other vegetables could Dr. Silverfish suggest that might cause people to stare and point? Draw a comic strip of Milo wearing three different vegetables and his attempts to explain why he's wearing them.

11. Critical Thinking

Stephen Manes, a very humorous author, created Dr. K. Pinkerton Silverfish, a very humorous fictional author whose humor is sometimes hard to judge. For example, in Dr. Silverfish's autobiography in chapter 2, is he joking about the degrees he holds from Fahrenheit University and Centigrade Institute? Yes! Stephen Manes is playing with words with double meanings. Obtain a copy of page 9 from your teacher to learn more about double meanings.

12. Language Arts

Make and then play "The Life of Milo Crinkley Game." Obtain a copy of the gameboard on page 10 from your teacher and glue it to a sheet of tagboard. Create five accident game cards, such as "The dog ate Milo's homework. Go back one space." Next, create five perfection game cards, such as "Milo didn't argue with his sister. Go forward two spaces." Ask a friend to play your game and remember: the first player to reach the finish line is the winner!

You Are What You Eat!

Complete the chart below to discover how your choices would compare to Milo's and how you both stack up to the Food Guide Pyramid.

1. List the foods Milo eats at the end of day two.	2. List the foods you would have eaten at the end of day two.

3. Read the Food Guide Pyramid below to find the recommended daily allowance of servings from each food group. Then record each item from above in the correct space next to the pyramid. **Hint:** Some foods will fit into more than one category; for example, bologna sandwich fits into grain (bread) and meat (bologna).

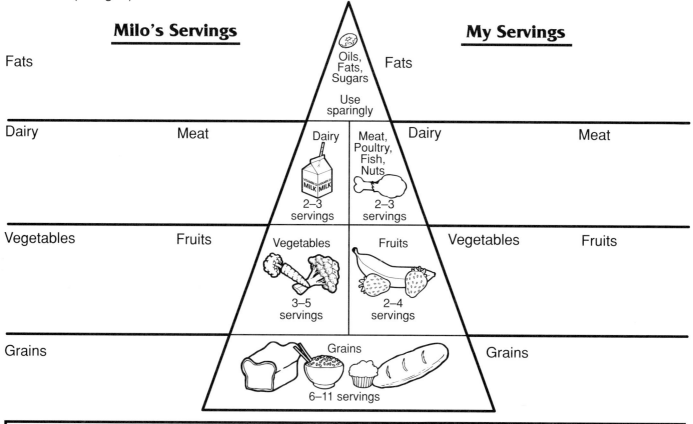

Milo's Servings   **My Servings**

Fats   Fats

Dairy   Meat   Dairy   Meat

Vegetables   Fruits   Vegetables   Fruits

Grains   Grains

Oils, Fats, Sugars — Use sparingly

Dairy — 2–3 servings

Meat, Poultry, Fish, Nuts — 2–3 servings

Vegetables — 3–5 servings

Fruits — 2–4 servings

Grains — 6–11 servings

4. Has Milo chosen a healthy balance of foods? If not, what should he have included or excluded?	5. Did you choose a healthy balance of foods? If not, what should you have included or excluded?

Note to the teacher: Use with activity #1 on page 6.

Double Time

In chapter 2, Stephen Manes plays with the double meanings of words and phrases. For example, he says that Dr. Silverfish holds college degrees, but when he gets tired, he puts them down. Holding a degree from college is not the same as holding something in your hands.

I. Directions: Read the 9 phrases below. In the spaces provided, draw a picture of the **actual** meaning of each phrase. Then write the **intended** meaning of each phrase on the lines provided. The first one has been done for you.

1. I held my tongue. I didn't say a word.	2. I'm counting on you.	3. The early bird catches the worm.
4. Please lend me a hand.	5. Don't count your chickens until they're hatched.	6. The pen is mightier than the sword.
7. The grass always looks greener on the other side.	8. If the shoe fits, wear it.	9. Time is money.

II. On the back of this sheet, make up three of your own phrases. Draw a picture of the actual meaning of each phrase. Then write the intended meaning of each phrase.

©2001 The Education Center, Inc. · *Contracts for Independent Readers* · *Humor* · TEC790 · Key p. 62

Note to the teacher: Use with activity #11 on page 7.

10

The Life of Milo Crinkley Game

Directions: Cut out the two broccoli squares. The first player uses the broccoli squares as dice by shaking them and dropping them on the desk. The player counts the broccoli squares lying face-up and moves that number of spaces. If none are face-up, the player loses a turn. If the player lands on a "draw a card" space, the player takes a card from the top of the stack and follows the directions given. Play proceeds until one player reaches Milo's classroom and is declared the winner!

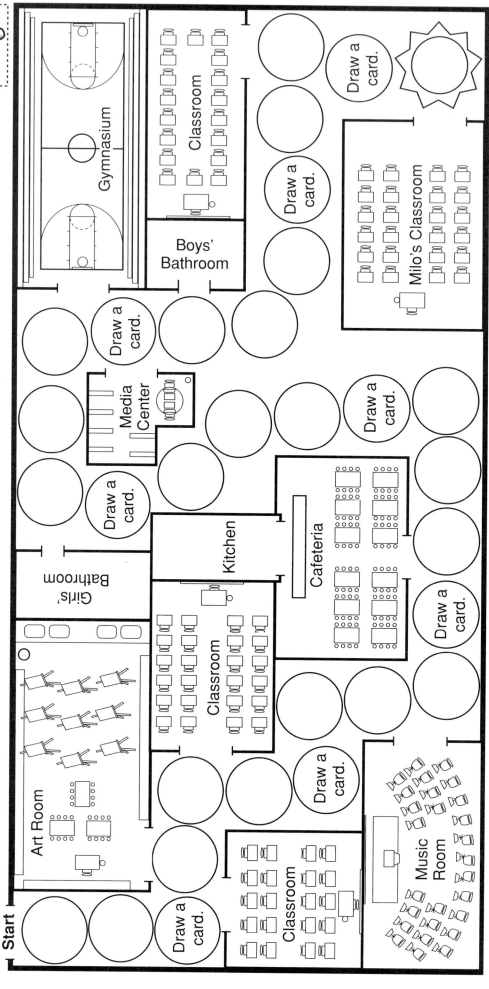

Note to the teacher: Use with activity #12 on page 7.

The Adventures of Captain Underpants

by Dav Pilkey

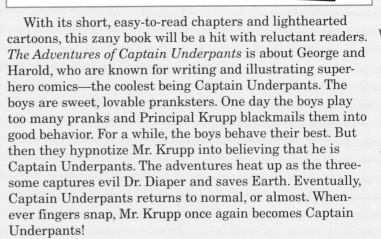

About the Book

With its short, easy-to-read chapters and lighthearted cartoons, this zany book will be a hit with reluctant readers. *The Adventures of Captain Underpants* is about George and Harold, who are known for writing and illustrating superhero comics—the coolest being Captain Underpants. The boys are sweet, lovable pranksters. One day the boys play too many pranks and Principal Krupp blackmails them into good behavior. For a while, the boys behave their best. But then they hypnotize Mr. Krupp into believing that he is Captain Underpants. The adventures heat up as the threesome captures evil Dr. Diaper and saves Earth. Eventually, Captain Underpants returns to normal, or almost. Whenever fingers snap, Mr. Krupp once again becomes Captain Underpants!

About the Author

According to Dav Pilkey, his first name can be pronounced any of three ways: as a rhyme with *rave* or *have* or *suave*. He has used the name Dav since 1983 when, as a waiter, he was given a nametag that was missing the final *e* from Dave.

Dav Pilkey was born March 4, 1966, in Cleveland, Ohio. He spent much of his early years laughing and drawing. That wasn't a problem until he started school. Dav became the class clown. His teachers sent him into the hall so often that he secretly stocked a desk with paper, pencils, and crayons. There Dav loved drawing and making up stories. Captain Underpants is a character Dav invented in 1973 while in the second grade. High school was tough but when Pilkey enrolled in college as an art major, things began to improve. He entered a contest for students who wrote and illustrated books. He won!

Pilkey's struggles in school were largely due to his attention deficit disorder and severe hyperactivity. He had reading disabilities that added to his difficulties. Because of this, Dav creates children's books with short chapters and many pictures to encourage reluctant readers to read.

Student Contract Materials List

- Activity #1: paper, pencil
- Activity #2: small boxes, paper towel tubes, glue, scissors, arts-and-crafts supplies
- Activity #3: paper, pencil
- Activity #4: copy of page 14, scissors, glue
- Activity #5: drawing paper, crayons or markers, magazine or newspaper ads
- Activity #6: drawing paper, crayons or markers
- Activity #7: drawing paper, crayons or markers
- Activity #8: reference materials on Bill Amend, Bill Watterson, Jim Davis, Charles Schulz, and Dav Pilkey
- Activity #9: drawing paper, scissors, stapler, crayons or markers
- Activity #10: copy of page 15
- Activity #11: copy of page 16
- Activity #12: poster board, crayons or markers, construction paper

The Adventures of Captain Underpants

Independent Contract

Name: _____   Number of activities to be completed: _____

1. Music

One of the outstanding pranks that George and Harold pull at school is to play "Weird Al" Yankovic music on the school intercom for six hours. "Weird Al" is famous for taking a well-known song and changing some of the words to make a funny, new meaning. For example, "Weird Al" followed up Michael Jackson's hit song "Beat It" with a recording titled "Eat It." Choose a song that is known by many people and rewrite the words to give it a new and funny meaning.

2. Art

The evil Dr. Diaper is determined to take over the world with his Laser-Matic 2000. Dr. Diaper designed the device to blow up the moon and make huge chunks fall on Earth. Fortunately, Captain Underpants stops Dr. Diaper and saves the day! Referring to the illustration of the Laser-Matic 2000 in chapter 15, create a model of the device.

3. Writing

You are the principal of Tuff Enuff Elementary School, which is considered the toughest school in the country. The former principal, who lasted only three weeks, was heard to mumble, "I want my mommy!" as he escaped through his office window. As the new principal, your first job is to get the school under control by posting a set of rules that all students must follow. Write a list of the ten most important rules you would enforce. Then write an announcement to Tuff Enuff students, describing the ways you would encourage students to follow your rules.

4. Language Arts

George and Harold write, illustrate, and publish their own comics. But one of their new comics is scrambled. Obtain a copy of page 14 from your teacher. Carefully follow the directions to get the comic in order and ready for publishing.

5. Social Studies

An old magazine ad for the Hypno-Ring gives hope to George and Harold as they trudge home after a day filled with working for Mr. Krupp. Study the ad pictured at the end of chapter 8. Notice the words that provide information and those that make the reader want to buy the item. Then notice how the picture grabs the reader's attention. Next, examine the words and pictures of a few ads in magazines or newspapers. Then, using what you have noticed, select a product (or make up one) to sell. Design a colorful ad for the product.

6. Writing

The old tree house is a special place that George and Harold rush to after school each day. They have comfortable furniture, a stockpile of junk food, and all the supplies needed for George to write stories and for Harold to draw pictures. What kind of place would be just right for you? Write a detailed description about a place you would like to go to after school. Include a description of where it would be located, how you would furnish it, what supplies you would keep there, and how you would use it. Then draw a picture or floor plan to illustrate your written description.

The Adventures of Captain Underpants
Independent Contract

Name:_____   Number of activities to be completed: _____

 Writing

George and Harold work as a team to produce the Captain Underpants comics. They spend hours doing what they love, drawing and writing, to create hundreds of comics. Give George and Harold some competition by creating an all-new comical superhero. Write humorous adventures in which your superhero fights an evil archenemy to save the day. Then illustrate your comic strip with your own cartoons.

 Research

What do Bill Amend, Bill Watterson, Jim Davis, Charles Schulz, and Dav Pilkey have in common? They have all become known as very successful cartoonists. Dav Pilkey, author of *The Adventures of Captain Underpants*, started writing and illustrating zany books when he was in elementary school. Is this typical of the other four cartoonists listed above? Research these men to find out how and when they became interested in cartooning. Prepare a presentation for the class, complete with samples of their work.

 Art

In chapter 16, George and Harold explain the art technique of Flip-O-Rama. Reread this section to become familiar with the details of this art form. Then create your own Flip-O-Rama. First, make a small booklet with at least six pages. Staple the pages together on the left side. Use scissors to trim the right edge. Then draw the same picture on each page, with the exception of one or two small parts that when flipped will show action.

 Language Arts

One prank that George and Harold enjoy is rewording messages on signs. With a quick and simple switch of a few letters, they change a school sign from "See Our Big Football Game Today" to "Boy Our Feet Smell Bad." Obtain a copy of page 15 from your teacher and see how clever you can be in changing the messages given into ones that are totally different.

 Math

George and Harold have some interesting math problems and a riddle to solve. Obtain a copy of page 16 from your teacher and follow the directions to discover the answer to the riddle.

 Critical Thinking

The crime-solving adventures of Captain Underpants in chapters 12 through 18 are great material for a gameboard. Reread this section and jot down the various setbacks that Captain Underpants faces as well as the problems he solves. Then plan a gameboard trail on which a player's advancement will be hindered by several spaces when he meets a villain or setback. Plan ways for the player to advance several spaces whenever he solves a crime. Draw the trail on poster board, decorate the board, write a set of directions, and then invite classmates to play.

14

Directions: Read and cut out each story line and speech bubble at the right. Look at each comic strip picture. Then glue each story line and speech bubble to its matching picture.

The Adventures of Captain Underpants

Story Lines

We were really angry!

Out of nowhere came Vac Man (who went around disguised as the school custodian)!

Two mean boys kicked us off the court!

We needed a plan.

It was a time of darkness and despair at Elwood Elementary School. Mean boys were taking over the playground.

Our plan wasn't working.

Who would have thought that Vac Man would save the day?

We put our plan into action.

Speech Bubbles

Hey! Who's this? It must be Vac Man!

Ha! Ha! Ha! Ha! Oh, I'm so afraid!

Hurrah for Vac Man!

They can't do this! This makes me really mad!

We need a big guy. I've got an idea!

Get out of here! We're taking over.

Hey, you big guys! Get off the court!

©2001 The Education Center, Inc. • *Contracts for Independent Readers • Humor • TEC790* • Key p. 62

Note to the teacher: Use with activity #4 on page 12.

Signs of Change

It looks like George and Harold have been scrambling messages again!

Directions: For each of the two signs below, fill in the blanks with letters from the original signs to discover the scrambled messages. **Hint**: Unused letters have been written on the trash cans to the right of the signs.

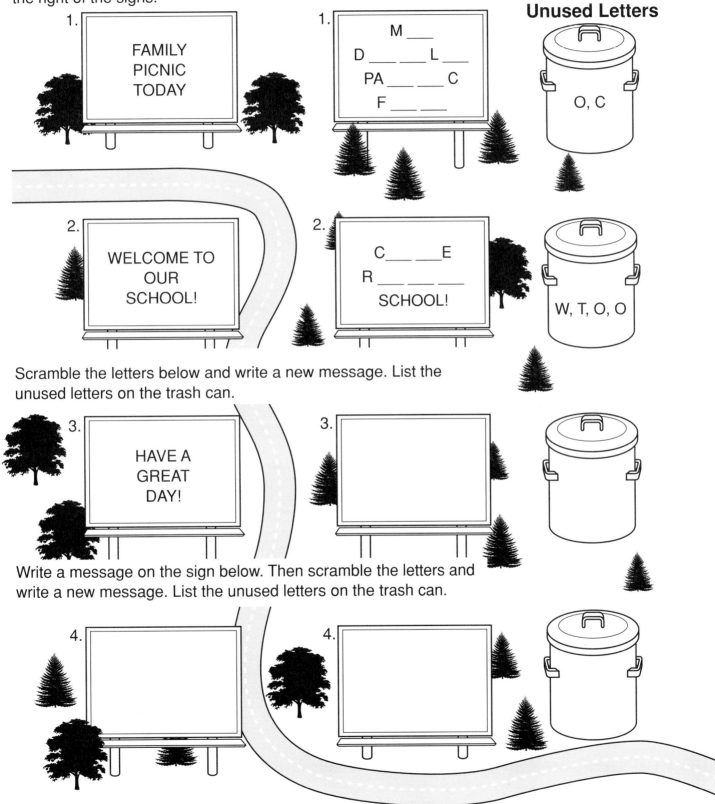

Unused Letters

1.
FAMILY
PICNIC
TODAY

1.
M ___
D ___ ___ L ___
PA ___ ___ C
F ___ ___

O, C

2.
WELCOME TO
OUR
SCHOOL!

2.
C ___ ___ E
R ___ ___ ___ ___
SCHOOL!

W, T, O, O

Scramble the letters below and write a new message. List the unused letters on the trash can.

3.
HAVE A
GREAT
DAY!

3.

Write a message on the sign below. Then scramble the letters and write a new message. List the unused letters on the trash can.

4.

4.

The Adventures of Captain Underpants

Go Figure!

What two things can Captain Underpants never eat for breakfast? Complete the activity below to find the answer.

Directions: Read each question below. Circle the letter under the correct answer. On the back of this page, show how you solved each problem.

George and Harold have a silly streak a mile long.

1. How long was their silly streak in feet?

5,820 feet	5,280 feet	8,520 feet
M	**H**	**G**

2. How long was their silly streak in inches?

63,360 inches	69,840 inches	62,400 inches
A	**B**	**Q**

George and Harold have been running amok in school for four long years.

3. How many weeks have they been running amok?

208 weeks	224 weeks	216 weeks
R	**Y**	**M**

4. How many days have they been running amok?
(Hint: One of those years was a leap year.)

1,464 days	4,381 days	1,461 days
O	**J**	**I**

After school George and Harold sell their comics for 50¢ each.

5. How much money would they earn if they sold 213 comics?

$10.65	$106.50	$1,065.00
S	**U**	**F**

6. How much money would they not earn if they lost 32 copies?

$1.60	$16.00	$160.00
K	**C**	**P**

George and Harold blasted "Weird Al" Yankovic songs for six hours straight.

7. How many minutes straight did they blast "Weird Al" Yankovic songs?

3,600 minutes	360 minutes	480 minutes
B	**E**	**V**

8. How many seconds straight did they blast "Weird Al" Yankovic songs?

3,600 seconds	360 seconds	21,600 seconds
T	**F**	**L**

Harold thinks they have to work for Mr. Krupp for eight more years.

9. How many months are in eight years of work?

416 months	96 months	80 months
W	**D**	**X**

10. How many weeks are in eight years of work?

32 weeks	768 weeks	416 weeks
Y	**Z**	**N**

Write the circled letter for each number shown below.

___ ___ ___ ___ ___ ___ ___ ___   ___ ___ ___ ___ ___
8   5   10 6   1   2   10 9   9   4   10 10 7   3

©2001 The Education Center, Inc. • *Contracts for Independent Readers • Humor* • TEC790 • Key p. 62

Note to the teacher: Use with activity #11 on page 13.

Amber Brown Is Feeling Blue

by Paula Danziger

About the Book

Amber Brown is a fourth grader learning to cope with life. In school, Amber has become accustomed to being the only girl with a two-color name in her class. That is until a new girl named Kelly Green arrives. At home, Mom and her friend Max plan for Amber to go with them to Walla Walla, Washington, for Thanksgiving. This plan seems exciting until Amber discovers that her dad will be arriving home from Paris and expects her to spend Thanksgiving with him in New York. She wants to do both, and she doesn't want to hurt either parent. All this leaves Amber feeling pretty blue. Slowly, with the help of her friends and the adults in her life, Amber learns to be content with her colorful, mixed-up life.

About the Author

Teens, preteens, and elementary school–aged children all know Paula Danziger, for she has written best-selling books for each of their age groups. What distinguishes her writing for all of these groups is her ability to take on serious problems—such as self-esteem, divorce, and social issues—with humor and grace.

Danziger was born on August 18, 1944, in Washington, DC. She was not an outstanding student, especially in her father's eyes, but she knew she wanted to be a writer. While she was young, Danziger started making mental notes of information she thought would be helpful in future writings.

Danziger graduated from Montclair State College in 1967 and began teaching. Although she enjoyed connecting with and inspiring many of her students, she left after three years. Later, while recovering from two serious car accidents, she wrote her first novel, *A Cat Ate My Gymsuit,* in an attempt to communicate with her former students. Danziger's goal is to write books that will touch the lives of children and make them feel less alone.

Student Contract Materials List

- Activity #1:   copy of page 20
- Activity #2:   white drawing paper, crayons or markers
- Activity #3:   large newsprint paper
- Activity #4:   2 T-shirts, fabric paint
- Activity #5:   crayons or markers
- Activity #6:   crayons or markers

- Activity #7:   paper grocery bag, scissors, crayons or markers, 1/2 sheet of poster board
- Activity #8:   paper, pencil
- Activity #9:   white drawing paper
- Activity #10: no materials needed
- Activity #11: copy of page 21, glue, 5 index cards, construction paper
- Activity #12: white drawing paper, crayons or markers

Amber Brown Is Feeling Blue

Independent Contract

Name:_____   Number of activities to be completed: _____

---

1. Language Arts

Amber Brown is very proud of her name. It is unusual, colorful, and—until Kelly Green shows up—unique. Do you know anyone who has a unique name? Parents and authors think seriously before naming a new baby or a new character. Some people may choose a name that signifies strength while others may wish to emphasize creativity. Some parents may prefer a name that sounds beautiful or rhythmic when spoken, while others may concentrate on a family name. Obtain a copy of page 20 from your teacher to discover different types of names.

2. Social Studies

Amber and her Amber-sitter, Brenda, are very close friends. In fact, Brenda tells Amber that if she had a sister she'd want her to be just like Amber, and Amber tells Brenda that she'd want a sister just like her. If you could pick someone to be a sister (or brother), whom would you choose? Draw a family portrait including your new sister or brother. On the back of the portrait, explain why you chose this person.

3. Writing

In chapter 8, Amber decides to alter her homework assignment from writing a boring research paper on the Middle Ages to publishing a creative Middle Ages newspaper. Reread chapter 8, paying close attention to the clever sections she has for her newspaper. Then design your own class or school newspaper, using Amber's as a guide.

4. Art

Amber and her Amber-sitter, Brenda, have very special T-shirts that they like to wear. If you could have T-shirts made for yourself and a special person in your life, what would you put on the shirts? Create a design for the two shirts. Then, with your parents' permission, paint two T-shirts with your designs.

5. Language Arts

The day after Halloween is not a great day for Amber Brown. It begins with Amber and her mother oversleeping and goes steadily downhill from there. Make a list of at least five things that go wrong in chapters 4 through 6. Think of a day in your life when things did not go well. Make a list of the things that went wrong for you. Then choose one thing from each list to illustrate. Write a caption under each picture explaining what went wrong.

6. Art

On Thanksgiving, Amber and her father go to New York City to see the famous Thanksgiving Day Parade. They see the giant helium balloons being inflated on Wednesday night outside the American Museum of Natural History. Amber jokes about the "stupid purple dinosaur" balloon. What kind of balloon do you think Amber would like? Design a balloon especially for older kids, like you and Amber, who come to view the parade.

Amber Brown Is Feeling Blue

Independent Contract

Name:_____ Number of activities to be completed: _____

7. Language Arts

When Mrs. Holt assigns a "Book Report in a Bag," Amber reads *The Watsons Go to Birmingham—1963,* by Christopher Paul Curtis. She uses a brown grocery bag for her report, and draws a picture from the story on the outside. Amber makes paper dolls of each character to place inside the bag. She then uses them to act out a scene. She also includes several other items to show the class as she presents the book. Use Amber's report as a model to do a "Book Report in a Bag" for *Amber Brown Is Feeling Blue.*

8. Writing

When Amber and Brandi go over to Kelly's house, Amber's mother drives them there. She likes to see where Amber goes when she doesn't know the people Amber is visiting. Amber qualifies this as a "Mom kind of thing to do." Are there certain things that most moms do? How about dads? Amber's dad always tells corny jokes. Take a survey of at least ten students. Ask them for things that they consider "mom" or "dad" kinds of things to do. Then write "A Guide to Parents," explaining the kinds of things parents do.

9. Art

Amber's dad sends her a "Countdown to Dad" book to prepare for his return from Paris. In this little book is a box for each day, with a picture and a place to check off the day when it is over. Lots of hearts are included to remind Amber that he loves her. Create your own countdown book for the next special event or holiday in your life. For each day, include a drawing and a message to remind you that your special day is coming!

10. Art

Amber's class is giving reports on the Pilgrims. Amber is barely able to focus her attention on the reports because she has so much on her mind. If the students were giving a pantomime instead of an oral report, Amber and the rest of her classmates would be forced to pay better attention. Select one scene from the book to *pantomime,* or act out with only body and facial movements.

11. Social Studies

Amber Brown has a colorful life, one that includes important places and events far and near. Some occasions are "mom events," and some are "dad events." All of them come together to make Amber who she is. Obtain a copy of page 21 from your teacher to discover all of the important "Amber-places." Next, glue page 21 to construction paper. Draw one illustration for each important location on an index card and then glue the cards around the outer edges of the paper.

12. Language Arts

Brenda, the Amber-sitter, is very creative when it comes to preparing food. It makes Amber a little nervous when Brenda announces that an amazing meal is being served. Reread the first part of chapter 1 to find out what Brenda prepares for the night before Halloween. Then create an illustrated "mischief menu" of your own. Include four dishes, a dessert, and something to drink. Label each item with what it really is, such as the cauliflower in the pumpkin, and what it is supposed to be (pumpkin's brains).

Name_____   *Amber Brown Is Feeling Blue*

A Perfect Match

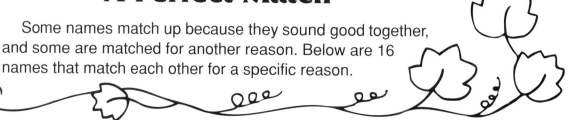

Some names match up because they sound good together, and some are matched for another reason. Below are 16 names that match each other for a specific reason.

I. Read each of the names listed below. Write each name in the corresponding box according to the type of words that make up the name. Amber Brown has been done for you.

Kelly Green	Melba Toast	April Shower	Bill Hill
Heather Branch	Sandy Beach	Summer Sun	Candy Apple
Otto Donato	Amber Brown	Rocky Mountain	August Heat
Joey Roo	Ivy Vine	Kitty Katz	Autumn Breeze

Colors	Rhymes	Animals	Plants
Amber Brown			
_____	_____	_____	_____
_____	_____	_____	_____

Food	Months	Seasons	Landscapes
_____	_____	_____	_____
_____	_____	_____	_____
_____	_____	_____	_____

II. Make up one name for each category above and write it in the appropriate box.

III. Choose one or more of the names above to use in a silly poem.

_____

_____

_____

_____

_____

_____

Note to the teacher: Use with activity #1 on page 18.

The Amber Maps

Find the special "Amber-places" by following the directions for each activity below.

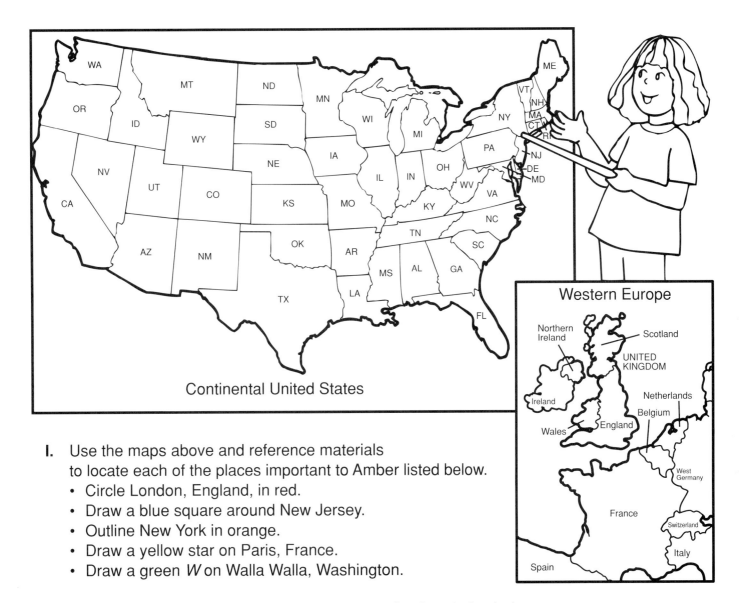

Continental United States

Western Europe

I. Use the maps above and reference materials
to locate each of the places important to Amber listed below.
- Circle London, England, in red.
- Draw a blue square around New Jersey.
- Outline New York in orange.
- Draw a yellow star on Paris, France.
- Draw a green *W* on Walla Walla, Washington.

II. Write the name of each location above next to its description below.

A. Amber lives here. _____

B. Amber and Dad go here to see the Thanksgiving Day Parade. _____

C. Mom and Max fly here to spend Thanksgiving with Max's sister Alice. _____

D. Dad has been living here. _____

E. Aunt Pam takes Amber here to meet Dad. _____

III. On index cards, draw an illustration showing why each location above is important in Amber's life.

Note to the teacher: Use with activity #11 on page 19.

How to Eat Fried Worms

by Thomas Rockwell

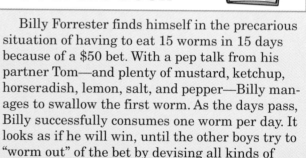

About the Book

Billy Forrester finds himself in the precarious situation of having to eat 15 worms in 15 days because of a $50 bet. With a pep talk from his partner Tom—and plenty of mustard, ketchup, horseradish, lemon, salt, and pepper—Billy manages to swallow the first worm. As the days pass, Billy successfully consumes one worm per day. It looks as if he will win, until the other boys try to "worm out" of the bet by devising all kinds of schemes to make Billy lose. Then Billy's family joins in to help him complete his mission.

About the Author

Thomas Rockwell was born March 13, 1933, in New Rochelle, New York. Rockwell, who had two brothers, grew up in rural Vermont. His father, Norman Rockwell, was a famous painter and illustrator. While both of his brothers were artistic, Rockwell drew his pictures with words. He attended Bard College, where he earned a B.A. degree in 1956. An avid reader as a child, it wasn't until Rockwell began reading to his young son that he was inspired to write children's literature. His first book, *Rackety-Bang and Other Verses,* was published in 1969. However, it was *How to Eat Fried Worms*, published in 1973, that brought him critical acclaim. Critics warned parents that the book might inspire copycat behavior in children, but also considered it a hilarious, original story. Rockwell stated it was not meant to be a funny book because "eating a worm is no joke."

Student Contract Materials List

- Activity #1: paper, pencil
- Activity #2: audiotape, tape recorder
- Activity #3: paper, pencil
- Activity #4: copy of page 25
- Activity #5: reference materials on worms, poster board, ten index cards, crayons or markers, glue, scissors
- Activity #6: reference materials on foods, white construction paper, crayons or markers

- Activity #7: copy of page 26
- Activity #8: stapler, crayons or markers
- Activity #9: paper, pencil
- Activity #10: reference materials on Pearl Harbor and Guadalcanal
- Activity #11: highlighter
- Activity #12: paper, pencil

How to Eat Fried Worms
Independent Contract

Name: _____   Number of activities to be completed: _____

 Language Arts (1.)

Alan dares Billy to eat 15 worms and then bets him $50 to do so in 15 days. Billy wonders where Alan got so much money. Alan states that he earns money by mowing lawns. How do you earn money? Brainstorm different ways students your age can earn money. Then make a list of the "25 Best Ways to Earn Money Without Eating Worms."

 Music (2.)

You wouldn't want to eat worms like Billy did, but you could write a song about the wiggly characters. Using the tune from the song "The Ants Go Marching," write a song based on *How to Eat Fried Worms.* Include ideas from the book, such as digging for worms, covering worms in condiments, and gulping them. Teach your song to a few friends and then tape-record it together.

 Language Arts (3.)

Eating worms is not an easy task for Billy. It is not the taste or even the texture that is so bad; the worst part is the thought of eating worms. Tom thinks of a clever idea to help Billy focus his thoughts on something he likes, such as fish. Then Tom creates a poem for Billy to recite to distract him from thoughts of worms (chapter 7). Tom's poem includes four nouns on the first line and a rhyming sentence on the second line; then Tom repeats the pattern to complete the poem. Using Tom's poem as a model, write an original poem that would keep your mind off something distasteful.

 Math (4.)

Billy thinks it will be worth eating 15 worms to win $50 from Alan. Billy dreams of the minibike he will buy when he wins the bet. Do you think Billy and Alan have made a good deal? Obtain a copy of page 25 from your teacher to decide which boy made the best deal.

 Science (5.)

Alan and Joe try to convince Billy that eating worms is dangerous to his health. Billy would not be concerned if he had studied earthworms. Research earthworms to discover ten interesting facts about them. Write the facts in the middle of ten different index cards. Then cut ten flaps in a large sheet of poster board. Glue one index card behind each flap so the fact can be seen when the flap is lifted. Decorate the poster board and write a title at the top.

 Social Studies (6.)

A bet entices Billy to eat something very unusual to him. To his surprise, he not only eats all 15 worms; he decides they are tasty, too. Many cultures incorporate food in their diet that may seem unusual to others, such as frogs' legs, pigs' feet, squid, and snails. Choose a food that is uncommon to you and then use it to plan a meal. Research where the food is commonly eaten, how it is prepared, and what to serve with it. Write your menu on a sheet of construction paper, including a description or illustration for each item.

How to Eat Fried Worms

Independent Contract

Name: _____ Number of activities to be completed: _____

 ## Reading

When two opposing teams are at battle, each one tries to develop strategies to assure a victory. Alan and Joe have declared a wormy battle against Billy and Tom. Alan and Joe try to keep Billy from eating 15 worms; Tom helps Billy eat the worms. During the battle Alan and Joe plan many attacks against Billy. In response, Tom and Billy execute clever counter-attacks. Obtain a copy of page 26 from your teacher and then keep score of the battles to discover which team is victorious.

 ## Writing

Billy smothers the cooked worms in ketchup, mustard, horseradish, lemon, salt, and pepper to eat them. Then his mother brainstorms different ways to prepare the worms. She suggests recipes such as Savory Worm Pie and Wormloaf with Mushroom Sauce. Eventually she makes a creation she names Whizbang Worm Delight. Brainstorm a list of at least eight different titles for worm recipes. Write each title on a separate sheet of paper and then complete each one with an ingredient list and cooking instructions. Finally, stack and then staple the recipe sheets together with a decorated cover titled "Wormy Cookbook."

 ## Critical Thinking

Billy is willing to choke down 15 worms to win enough money to buy the minibike of his dreams. The minibike must be spectacular for Billy to agree to such drastic measures. Make a list of things you would like to acquire. Study the list, decide which one is the most important, and then circle it. Write a list of ideas titled "The Silliest Things I Would Do to Get a _____." Then decide if you would really do one of these things. Write a paragraph explaining why or why not.

 ## Social Studies

Thomas Rockwell includes interesting chapter titles, such as "Pearl Harbor" (chapter 25), and "Guadalcanal" (chapter 26) in the book. Keep in mind that this story resembles a war, with attacks and counterattacks being staged by the boys. Research the World War II battles of Pearl Harbor and Guadalcanal between the United States and Japan. Then decide which boy in the book symbolizes the United States and which boy symbolizes Japan. Write an explanation and then present it to the class as a television nightly news program.

 ## Language Arts

Alan is confident that there is no way he could lose the bet he has made with Billy. However, Billy is stubborn enough to do whatever it takes to win the bet, even eating worms. So Alan and Joe try to trick Billy into failure. In chapter 31 the boys attempt to convince Billy that eating worms is hazardous to his health by sending a fake letter from Dr. McGrath. Copy the letter, highlighting the mistakes, and then rewrite it with corrections.

 ## Writing

In chapter 7, Tom and Billy use their imaginations to concoct a minibike story with themselves as the main characters. Their story is so wild that in the end they have to run away and join the navy to escape punishment. Reread the boys' adventurous tale and then imagine you have a minibike too. Write a story about a dangerous mission, including a quick getaway on your minibike.

The Dollars and Sense of Eating Worms

4. Alan calculates that it will cost $8 to trick Billy into missing worm number 12. About how much does each worm actually cost?

_____

5. Alan has to work every Saturday for the next six months (26 total) to earn $50. How much will he earn each Saturday?

_____

6. Alan loses his $2.50 weekly allowance for two weeks as well as the $50.00 for the bet. Alan also spends $8.00 to trick Billy into missing worm number 12. What is the total cost of losing the bet?

_____

3. If Billy agrees to eat one worm a day for 30 days, how much money will he earn?

_____

2. Billy brags that he can eat 20 worms. If Alan paid Billy the same amount per worm, how much would Alan owe him?

_____

9. Do you think Alan makes a good deal? Why?

_____
_____
_____

7. If Billy convinces someone to bet him $5 per worm, how much money will he earn for eating 15 worms?

_____

1. Billy eats 15 worms for $50. About how much does he earn for each worm?

_____

8. Do you think Billy makes a good deal when he decides to take Alan's bet? Why?

_____
_____
_____

Note to the teacher: Use with activity #4 on page 23.

Strategy for Success

Game plans have been made and the two teams are ready for battle. Read the strategies and counterstrategies below and then decide which team earns a point. The first one is done for you. Total the points to determine which team is strategically successful. Then write your own strategy and counterstrategy in the space provided.

	Team #1: Alan and Joe	Points	Team #2: Billy and Tom	Points
1.	Want to dig in the manure to pick the first worm.	0	Protest, so Alan and Joe let Tom pick the spot to dig the worm.	1
2.	Pick out a huge night crawler.		Check the dictionary for clarification.	
3.	Tell a dramatic story to scare Billy.		Don't believe the story.	
4.	Try to impose a time limit.		Beat the time limit.	
5.	Glue two worms together.		Discover the trick.	
6.	Tell Billy's mom.		Mom develops worm recipes.	
7.	Take Billy to Shea Stadium and then bring him home late.		Billy wakes up just in time to find a worm to eat.	
8.	Send a phony letter from Dr. McGrath.		Dad tells them it is a fake letter.	
9.	Make a worm with beans.		Billy discovers the trick.	
10.	Lock Billy inside a closet.		Dad lets him out.	
11.	Plan to lower Billy into the cistern.		Dad stops them.	

Total _____   Total _____

Your Strategy	Your Counterstrategy
_____	_____
_____	_____
_____	_____
_____	_____
_____	_____

With the strategy and counterstrategy you added, which team would get the extra point?

_____

Owls in the Family

by Farley Mowat

About the Book

Billy lives with his mother, father, and an assortment of pets, such as rats, snakes, and a dog. One might think that Billy has plenty of pets, but when two owls enter his life, he manages to love and nurture them as well. Billy and his two friends rescue the owl Wol and two weeks later Billy rescues Weeps. Then the entertainment really begins. Wol has a unique way of turning a situation upside down, as when he flies into Billy's classroom and skids across the teacher's desk. Weeps reaches his potential as a comical little owl who learns a great deal, except how to fly. This enjoyable story is both funny and loving with solid characters and memorable pets.

About the Author

Farley Mowat was born in Belleville, Ontario, Canada, on May 12, 1921. As a boy, Farley was small for his age, he moved frequently, and his interests were bird watching and writing. He was more popular with his teachers than with his peers. Since his father was a librarian, Farley spent a lot of time in the library. His father encouraged Farley's reading and writing. At about ten years of age, Farley sent a sample of his writing to the *Prairie Pals,* a weekly kids' supplement in the local paper. They liked it so much that they gave him a regular column. With some of his friends, Farley started a club for kids interested in nature and the environment.

From 1939 to 1946, Mowat served in the Canadian army. His service during the war was particularly difficult for him. One of the ways he coped was by writing. *The Dog Who Wouldn't Be* was written during that period. Following those years, Mowat became a government biologist in Northern Canada. Farley Mowat has written extensively, both fiction and nonfiction, for juvenile and adult readers. Much of his writing deals with topics about nature and the environment.

Student Contract Materials List

- Activity #1: paper, pencil
- Activity #2: reference materials on pet care, 4 lunch bags, 4 large index cards, permanent markers
- Activity #3: copy of page 30
- Activity #4: crayons or markers, drawing paper
- Activity #5: copy of page 31
- Activity #6: paper, pencil
- Activity #7: reference materials on horned owls, crows, and skunks; drawing paper; art supplies

- Activity #8: a paper plate, a stapler, scissors, drawing paper, markers
- Activity #9: drawing paper
- Activity #10: copy of page 32
- Activity #11: reference materials on owls, drawing paper, scissors, markers
- Activity #12: paper, pencil

Owls in the Family

Independent Contract

Name: _____ Number of activities to be completed: _____

1. Language Arts

Poetry often expresses feelings. Billy feels very strongly about his pets, especially Wol and Weeps. Follow the pattern below to write a diamonte poem about Wols, Weeps, or a pet of your own.

one noun
two adjectives
three verbs
four nouns
three verbs
two adjectives
one noun

2. Research

Billy has a lot of pets and spends many hours caring for them. Select four animals that people have as pets, such as dogs and birds. Research pet care for the four animals. Write about each animal's care on a large index card. Then staple the bottom of four lunch bags together. Draw a picture of each animal on each of the lunch bags. Next, place each index card in its matching bag. Finally, write a title on the first bag. Place this handy pet care booklet in your classroom library.

3. Math

In the beginning of chapter 2, Billy's father is concerned that Billy wants to add an owl to his family of pets. Billy has many pets, but exactly how many he has varies from day to day. Some days a pigeon will bring home a relative or two, and the rats have so many babies so often that it's hard to keep count. Obtain a copy of page 30 from your teacher. Follow the directions and figure out how many pets Billy could end up with in a year.

4. Art

Every summer Billy's family spends two weeks camping near Dundurn. His father has built a special caravan, called Mowat's Prairie Schooner, which they pull behind their convertible Model A Ford. The Mowat family is quite a sight with all their pets and belongings. Read the description of their caravan in chapter 10. Then, using Billy's description, create a drawing of what you think the caravan looks like. Show the Model A Ford with the rumble seat pulling the caravan.

5. Social Studies

Owls in the Family takes place in Saskatoon, Saskatchewan, a quiet place for Billy and his friends to grow up. When the boys cross over the railroad bridge, they are on the prairie. The open, undeveloped land where they can catch gophers and sight birds gives them a feeling of freedom. To better understand where Billy lives, obtain a copy of page 31 from your teacher.

6. Writing

In chapter 9, Wol terrorizes three people with whom he comes in contact: the minister who comes to visit, the mailman who accidentally kicks Wol, and Billy's French teacher. Keeping Wol's personality in mind as well as the sheer size of a great horned owl, write a short story in which Wol terrorizes someone in your life. Keep your story humorous and fun.

Owls in the Family
Independent Contract

Name: _____ Number of activities to be completed: _____

Writing

7.

Billy Mowat, narrator of *Owls in the Family*, tells about his boyhood adventures with all kinds of animals. However, the two horned owls are the real stars of the story. While most people fear the owls because of their size and strength, to Billy they are simply part of the family. Read about horned owls and their enemies, crows and skunks. Then write and illustrate a picture book about an owl's adventure. Use the information you have gathered to write your story.

Social Studies

8.

Reread chapters 1 and 2 for a description of where Billy grows up. Then create a pocketful of prairie illustrations. First, fold and cut a paper plate in half. Staple the rounded edges together to create a pocket. Label the front "Saskatoon" and illustrate the prairie, adding details from the story. Then fold a sheet of drawing paper into fourths and cut out the resulting rectangles. On each rectangle, illustrate an item described, such as a cottonwood tree. Then turn each illustration over and write about a similar item found in your area. Place the completed illustrations in the paper-plate pocket.

Language Arts

9.

In chapter 6, Billy learns that a local department store is sponsoring a pet parade. Billy and his friends, Bruce and Murray, enter in hopes of winning some prizes. The parade ends up becoming a hilarious event. Pretend that you are a local news reporter who is assigned to cover the parade. Write a front-page newspaper article with a catchy headline. Then draw a picture to represent a photograph of the event.

Reading

10.

Did you ever hear the word *ructions* before? How about *slough*? Author Farley Mowat uses some vocabulary that may be new to you. Sometimes we can figure out the meaning of a new word by the way it is used in a sentence. Instead of reading over unfamiliar words, see if you can discover their meaning. Obtain a copy of page 32 from your teacher and find the real meanings among the silly ones.

Science

11.

Wol and Weeps are horned owls that have been rescued from the wild. Farley Mowat introduces some interesting information about horned owls in his book *Owls in the Family*. Research four different kinds of owls to find out about their habitats, diets, nesting habits, and birthing behaviors. Then fold a sheet of drawing paper into fourths and cut out the resulting rectangles. On each rectangle, design a stamp that illustrates a different owl you researched. Then write a persuasive letter to an imaginary postmaster, telling him about each owl and why the illustrations should be used as stamp designs.

Writing

12.

One of Billy's favorite games to play when he first gets Wol and Weeps is can-the-can. It is made up of parts of baseball and parts of football. Billy plays it with a bunch of neighborhood kids in an empty lot. When they play this game, Wol gets right into the excitement. Invent your own exciting version of can-the-can. Write directions on how the game is played, along with the rules and instructions for keeping score.

Name_____

Keeping Count

Directions: Use the information in the first three columns to figure out the lowest number and the highest number of pets Billy could have at the end of one year from one female of each species.

Pet	Number of babies per litter	Number of litters per year	Lowest number of babies per year	Highest number of babies per year
1. gopher	3–6	1	_____	_____
2. rat	6–12	3–6	_____	_____
3. pigeon	2	5–11	_____	_____
4. garter snake	7–85	1	_____	_____
5. dog	2–12	2	_____	_____
6. rabbit	4–5	1–5	_____	_____
7. owl	2–3	1	_____	_____

Totals _____   _____

Using the chart above, answer the following questions.

8. What is the lowest number of babies a female rat might have in four years?

_____

The highest? _____

9. What is the lowest number of babies a pigeon might have in five years?

_____

The highest? _____

10. A social group of rabbits has 1–7 females in it. What is the lowest number of babies that might be born in the social group in a year?

_____

The highest? _____

Note to the teacher: Use with activity #3 on page 28.

Bird's-Eye View of Canada

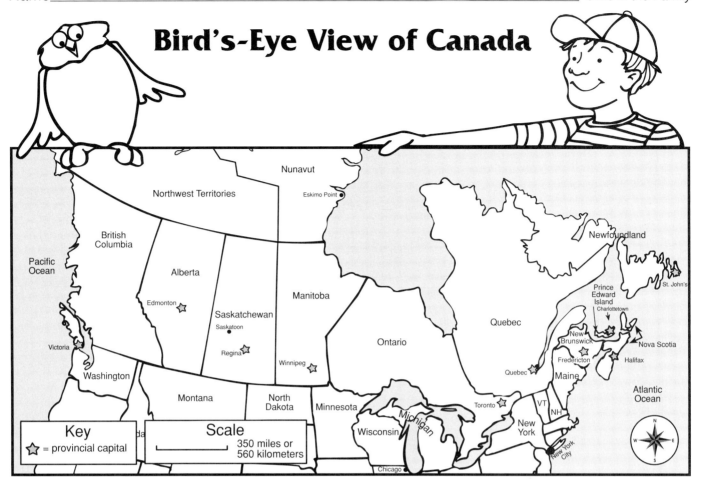

Directions: Refer to the map to answer the following questions.

1. Which ocean borders Canada and the United States on the west?_____

2. Which Canadian province is west of Saskatchewan? _____ East? _____

3. Which U.S. states border Saskatchewan? _____

4. Billy moved from Saskatoon to Toronto, Canada. What is the approximate distance between Toronto and Saskatoon in miles? _____ In kilometers? _____

5. What is the approximate distance between Saskatoon and Chicago? _____ Saskatoon and New York City? _____

6. When traveling from Saskatchewan to the U.S., in what direction would one travel?

   _____

7. What is the capital of Saskatchewan? _____

8. About how many miles is it from Saskatoon to the capital of New Brunswick? _____

Double Time

Directions: Read each sentence and the definitions that follow it. Draw an *X* in the box beside the definition that best explains the underlined word. Then write why the other definition is a silly choice.

Example: Billy carefully placed the owl in his <u>haversack</u> with his schoolbooks and slung it over his shoulder.

X A. a bag worn over one shoulder

☐ B. a pair of men's trousers with no pockets

<u>It doesn't make sense that Billy would put an owl and schoolbooks into a pair of trousers and then sling them over his shoulder.</u>

1. Walking through the <u>slough</u>, Billy saw about a thousand ducks.
   ☐ A. the side aisles in a movie theater
   ☐ B. a swamp; backwater; a creek in a marsh

   _____

2. An Indian lent Billy a <u>cayuse</u> and Billy rode it across the prairie.
   ☐ A. a native range horse
   ☐ B. a hand-carved canoe

   _____

3. The boys knew Mr. Miller would hide in the <u>blind</u> until an owl showed up.
   ☐ A. an enclosure in which a person can hide to shoot game or observe wildlife
   ☐ B. a window shade made of thin, metal slats

   _____

4. The <u>chinooks</u> arrived and tossed many bird nests out of trees.
   ☐ A. a warm, dry wind that descends the eastern slopes of the Rocky Mountains
   ☐ B. politicians who don't support environmental issues

   _____

5. Wol's dropping a dead skunk caused quite a <u>ruction</u> for the family.
   ☐ A. a disturbance or uproar
   ☐ B. a time of joy and peace

   _____

6. Sometimes Wol could be as <u>ornery</u> as a mule.
   ☐ A. attractive
   ☐ B. irritable

   _____

7. Billy and his pets traveled in a <u>caravan</u> to the lake every summer for two weeks of vacation.
   ☐ A. a well-padded cardboard box for shipping long distances
   ☐ B. trailer

   _____

8. The <u>burrows</u> of the gophers on the prairie made the field look like it had the measles.
   ☐ A. holes in the ground made by an animal
   ☐ B. the tough skins of wild animals

   _____

   _____

Summer Reading Is Killing Me!
by Jon Scieszka

About the Book

Just as Sam and Fred are trying to make Joe promise not to open *The Book* at all during summer vacation, the Time Warp Trio gets sucked into its seventh adventure in this incredibly popular series. The trio gets transplanted into the middle of *The Hoboken Chicken Emergency,* one of the books on their summer reading list. To make matters worse, characters from all of the books on the list are converging on the Hoboken library, where the bad guys are plotting to wipe out the good guys and take over their stories. The boys realize they have to immediately find *The Book* to end this precarious situation before children's literature is destroyed forever.

About the Author

Jon Scieszka was born on September 8, 1954, in Flint, Michigan. He is the second oldest of six boys. He says that he has always wanted to be an author.

Scieszka studied to be a doctor at Albion College in Michigan, and he studied writing at Columbia University in New York. He  planned to write the great American novel. Instead, he taught in an elementary school for ten years, getting to know how kids think. He discovered that kids love a joke that twists the expected into the unexpected. Scieszka writes books that fall somewhere between picture books and chapter books—books that reluctant readers will pick up and enjoy. He says that his audience is the "hardcore silly kids"!

Scieszka is married and has two children of his own, a son and a daughter. He has written many books for youngsters, including *The True Story of the Three Little Pigs!*, *The Stinky Cheese Man and Other Fairly Stupid Tales*, and *Math Curse*.

Student Contract Materials List

- Activity #1: white drawing paper, crayons or markers
- Activity #2: white drawing paper, crayons or markers
- Activity #3: white drawing paper, crayons or markers
- Activity #4: 2 sheets of 8½" x 11" blue construction paper, silver marker or crayon
- Activity #5: paper, pencil

- Activity #6: copy of page 36, crayons or markers
- Activity #7: copy of page 37
- Activity #8: crayons or markers
- Activity #9: paper, pencil
- Activity #10: copy of page 38, crayons or markers
- Activity #11: paper, pencil
- Activity #12: construction paper, crayons or markers

Summer Reading Is Killing Me!

Independent Contract

Name:_____   Number of activities to be completed: _____

1. Language Arts

"What building has the most stories?" It's not the Empire State Building! It's the library! Sam, the joke and riddle brainiac, shows off his talent when he quizzes his audience with some of his jokes. Reread the jokes he shares in chapters 1, 2, and 7. Then make a joke book in which you write and illustrate your ten favorite jokes.

2. Writing

Sam, Joe, and Fred are quite overwhelmed when they see some of the characters from books they have read. Imagine seeing Frog and Toad, or Charlotte from *Charlotte's Web.* Which character would you most like to meet? Create a comic strip about a meeting you have with your favorite storybook character. Include all of the details about this exciting meeting.

3. Art

In chapter 6, Joe compares seeing all the storybook characters wandering around to the way a person usually visualizes a character in his mind when reading about him. Have you ever read a story in which a character is described so well that you form a mental picture of that character without seeing any illustrations? Draw a picture of a character you have visualized. On the back of the paper, write the character's name and the title of the story in which he belongs. Then ask several classmates to guess who it is.

4. Social Studies

A book that Joe's uncle gives him is the source of the boys' adventures. Whenever they open *The Book,* they go places—from the Stone Age to the future. There is magic inside the dark blue book with strange silver writing on it. All books are magical because they take you on journeys in your imagination. Write an imaginative story about time travel. Then make a special book cover for it, modeling the cover of *The Book.* Use a silver crayon or marker to decorate and title it.

5. Writing

A key element in this zany book is the summer reading list. It is the source of all the characters that come to the Hoboken library. Had Fred not stuck it in *The Book,* all the crazy events that take place would never have happened. It should not come as a surprise, then, that the list itself is a bit zany. Carefully reread the summer reading list on the last four pages of *Summer Reading Is Killing Me!* to see what surprises you discover. Then come up with your own summer reading list of at least ten titles that you would highly recommend. Include a few surprises of your own!

6. Language Arts

In chapter 9, Joe, Sam, and Fred encounter a girl. They are not sure who she is because they haven't read any girls' books. Perhaps they believe that all girls' books are boring. Many readers would strongly disagree with this view of girls' books, but there might be other types of books they think are boring. Obtain a copy of page 36 from your teacher to find out whether some categories of books are enjoyed more than others.

Summer Reading Is Killing Me!

Independent Contract

Name:_____ Number of activities to be completed: _____

7. Language Arts

Jon Scieszka, author of *Summer Reading Is Killing Me!*, cleverly incorporates characters from the books on the trio's summer reading list into the story. The boys can identify some of the characters quite easily, but others are unknown to them. How many could you identify if you were in their place? Obtain a copy of page 37 from your teacher to test your knowledge of books, authors, and characters!

8. Writing

This latest Time Warp Trio adventure looks dramatically different from the others. It is the first time that characters from many books come together in one place. Joe quickly realizes the danger of the situation. What if an evil character from one story decides to destroy the main character from another story? What if imaginary creatures invade a story from history? Have some fun thinking about the mix-up that would be created by a character from one book finding his or her way into another book. Use your imagination and write a mixed-up character story with illustrations.

9. Writing

The Hoboken Public Library is the scene of a near disaster the day the book characters escape from their books and gather to change the whole landscape of literature. Mr. Bear, the soft, fuzzy teddy bear looking for a new image, is trying to eliminate all of the nice characters and take over their books. Imagine that you are working quietly in a back corner of the library. You are an eyewitness to the entire event. Write a front-page news article describing what you saw and heard in the library that day. Give your article an attention-getting title.

10. Critical Thinking

Fred is crazy about street skating. In chapter 2, when Sam tries to convince Fred and Joe to get their summer reading done right away, Fred counters with all the skating moves he wants to practice. Although Fred doesn't get to practice his skating moves exactly as he thinks he might, his talent does come in handy when he does a "one-eighty monkey plant to an alley-oop fishbrain into a mistyflip rocket air" to grab *The Book* and save the day. If this sounds like a foreign language, obtain a copy of page 38 to master skating lingo.

11. Writing

In *Summer Reading Is Killing Me!* all of the characters from the summer reading list have come together in the Hoboken Public Library. The story is told from the viewpoint of Joe, Sam, and Fred, who are trying to get the characters back in their own books. But how would this story be described from the viewpoint of one of the storybook characters? Rewrite one of the scenes from the book from the point of view of one of the storybook characters, such as Mr. Bear, Long John Silver, or Eeyore.

12. Art

In chapter 8, the reader learns that the teddy bear is the mastermind behind this terrible plot. The bear, "Mr. Bear to you," is tired of being cute, cuddly, and dumb. He wants respect, so he tries to take over and make himself and the bad characters the new main characters of well-known books. Choose four of your favorite books. How would they change if Mr. Bear became the main character of each book? Make a poster illustrating the four new book covers, showing Mr. Bear as the new main character of each.

Reader's Choice Survey

Find out what types of books interest your friends and family with this reader's choice survey.

Directions: Read the types of books listed in the table below. Then survey your friends and family to find out if they think each type of book is enjoyable or boring. Make a tally mark in the appropriate column for each response. Then, in the last two columns, calculate the total for each row.

Book Types	Enjoyable	Boring	Enjoyable Total	Boring Total
Humor				
Fantasy				
Mystery				
Adventure				
Historical Fiction				
Realistic Fiction				
Science Fiction				

Use the totals from above to complete the pie graphs below.

Directions: Create a pie graph by dividing the first circle below into appropriate divisions according to your enjoyable totals above. Color the pie so that each section is a different color. Then lightly color the corresponding box above to match. Create a second pie graph by repeating the directions for your boring totals.

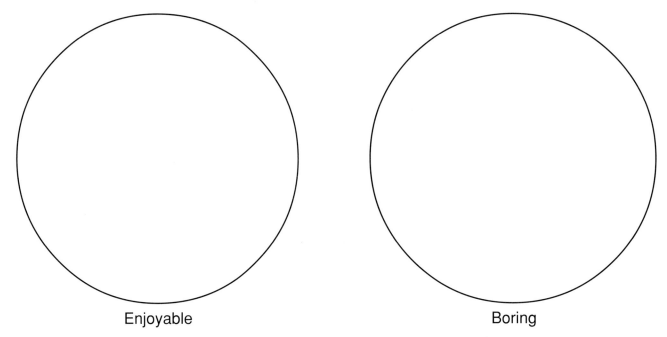

Enjoyable   Boring

Literary IQ

Test your knowledge of titles, authors, and characters.
Do you know as many as Joe, Sam, and Fred?

Directions: Read the list of titles and characters in the boxes below.
Then, in the spaces provided, write the book title and character next
to the corresponding author.

Title
Alice in Wonderland
Robin Hood
Moby Dick
The House at Pooh Corner
The Lion, the Witch, and the Wardrobe
The Tale of Peter Rabbit
Matilda
The Legend of Sleepy Hollow
Gods, Heroes, and Men of Ancient Greece
Adventures of Tom Sawyer
The Hoboken Chicken Emergency
Treasure Island

Character
The Trunchbull
Henrietta
Red Queen
Captain Ahab
Long John Silver
Mr. McGregor
Sheriff of Nottingham
White Witch
Headless Horseman
Injun Joe
Eeyore
Cyclops

Author	Title	Character
1. C. S. Lewis		
2. Beatrix Potter		
3. Rosemary Sutcliff		
4. Washington Irving		
5. Roald Dahl		
6. Herman Melville		
7. Robert Louis Stevenson		
8. Lewis Carroll		
9. A. A. Milne		
10. Daniel Manus Pinkwater		
11. Mark Twain		
12. W. H. D. Rouse		

Street-Skating Lingo

Become a master of street-skating lingo by solving the crossword puzzle below.
Hint: Each word in the box will be used once.

stride	cadence	toe-flicking	fakie
scissor	crossover	drafting	glide

Across
1. Skating behind another skater to lessen the amount of wind resistance
2. Pushing off with your toe at the end of a stride
3. To place one skate directly in front of the other
4. A pushing of one leg behind the other in order to turn quickly and speed up while turning

Down
5. The speed (rate) of a skater's strides
6. A prefix added to a term for a trick and meaning "to do the trick backward"
7. To roll on one skate while the other skate recovers from the stride
8. To push outward to the side to increase speed

Draw a picture of what you think these eight street-skating tricks look like.

1. one-eighty monkey plant	2. mistyflip rocket air	3. alley-oop fishbrain	4. glide
5. toe-flicking	6. drafting	7. crossover	8. scissor

©2001 The Education Center, Inc. • *Contracts for Independent Readers* • Humor • TEC790 • Key p. 63

38   **Note to the teacher:** Use with activity #10 on page 35.

Tales of a Fourth Grade Nothing

by Judy Blume

About the Book

Being a fourth grader with a two-and-one-half-year-old brother is not an easy life. Peter is the only one in the family who does not think Fudge, his brother, is incredibly cute. Peter feels that his mom and dad forget he is a member of the family, except when they need his help to get Fudge to cooperate. Peter is expected to stand on his head for Fudge, literally. Meanwhile, Fudge invades his privacy, ruins his things, and even eats his turtle. Why don't Mom and Dad realize that Peter would like a little respect too? In the end, all of the injustices are forgiven when Dad brings home a dog—just for Peter.

About the Author

Judy Blume was born February 12, 1938, in Elizabeth, New Jersey. Growing up, she created stories while playing with paper dolls, practicing the piano, and playing ball. Although she never wrote these stories down or even told anyone about them, her love and desire to make up stories continued to grow. After her own two children started preschool she began to write—and 20-plus books and dozens of awards later, she's still going strong.

Blume has written books for many different age groups, but the constant in them all is her ability to develop very real and identifiable characters. Blume feels that she has a talent of being able to recall what it was like to be a child at various stages in her own life. She has an incredible memory and draws on it to help enliven her characters to feel the true emotions of that age. She writes honestly, openly, and directly about issues that children can relate to, such as self-confidence, sibling rivalry, and social ostracism. Blume's ideas come from her imagination; events from her childhood; and things she reads, sees, and hears.

Student Contract Materials List

- Activity #1: reference materials on New York City transportation, construction paper, crayons or markers
- Activity #2: white drawing paper, crayons or markers, magazines, scissors, glue
- Activity #3: 5 sheets of colorful paper, arts-and-crafts supplies
- Activity #4: nutrition guide
- Activity #5: construction paper, crayons or markers
- Activity #6: copy of page 42, highlighter

- Activity #7: construction paper, crayons or markers
- Activity #8: paper, pencil
- Activity #9: reference materials on New England, white drawing paper, crayons or markers
- Activity #10: copy of page 43
- Activity #11: paper, pencil
- Activity #12: copy of page 44, six 4" x 6" index cards, string, hole puncher, scissors, glue

Tales of a Fourth Grade Nothing

Independent Contract

Name:_____ Number of activities to be completed: _____

1. Art

Mrs. Haver, Peter's teacher, assigns projects related to New York City to her students. Peter, Jimmy, and Sheila are assigned the topic of transportation. They decide that Sheila will make a booklet while Peter and Jimmy make a poster. Work progresses smoothly until Fudge gets into Peter's room and destroys the poster. Research New York City's different forms of transportation. Then make a poster to replace the one Fudge ruins. Include an illustration and a brief description of each type of transportation available.

2. Language Arts

Shoe shopping with Fudge is not a pleasant experience! In chapter 6, Fudge has a temper tantrum right in the shoe store and Peter is mortified. Perhaps if Mrs. Hatcher had done a little catalog shopping with Fudge instead, the whole embarrassing situation could have been avoided. Design a catalog page featuring shoes. Draw, or cut out and glue, ten different kinds of shoes, including loafers and brown-and-white saddle shoes. Write a short description below each picture, giving details about the shoes, the price, and why someone would want to buy them.

3. Social Studies

This book contains a record of many events in Peter's life. Some people record their memories in scrapbooks. Using a combination of illustrations, decorative borders, and colorful paper, create a five-page scrapbook for Peter. Highlight one event from the book on each page. Add captions and titles for each event.

4. Science

In chapter 3, Fudge stops eating. After the third day, Mrs. Hatcher starts experimenting with different kinds of food, hoping to get him to eat. What foods would entice you to eat, if you decided to stop eating? Make a list of your favorite foods and rank them in order from your most favorite to your least favorite. Next, divide them into the four main food groups—meat and poultry, dairy, fruits and vegetables, and grains and cereals. Then write a letter to one of your parents explaining how to use the list to prepare an enticing, well-balanced meal in case you decide to stop eating.

5. Social Studies

Peter feels as if he is totally unimportant. It seems to Peter that everyone thinks whatever Fudge does is cute. Peter thinks that whatever Fudge does is so annoying. Why doesn't anyone appreciate Peter? He just wants to be recognized for what he goes through as Fudge's older brother. Create a Brother of the Year award for Peter. Then create a Brother or Sister of the Year award for someone you know who is a good older brother or sister. (Maybe your older brother or sister!) On the back of each award write a paragraph explaining why that person deserves the award.

6. Social Studies

The Hatcher family lives at 25 West 68th Street, New York, New York. This part of New York City is known as Manhattan. From their apartment house, they can walk to the park, stores, theaters, and the zoo. Many people choose to live in Manhattan because there are so many interesting things to do. Obtain a copy of page 42 from your teacher. Study the map of the city and then follow the directions to get a better idea of where Peter lives.

Tales of a Fourth Grade Nothing

Independent Contract

Name: _____ Number of activities to be completed: _____

---

7. Art

Henry is the elevator operator in Peter's apartment building. Henry knows that Peter lives on the 12th floor. Peter is impressed by how much Henry knows about the people that live in the building. Imagine the interesting people that live there. Draw a picture of what you think Peter's apartment building looks like. In each window show something interesting happening to one of Peter's neighbors. Don't forget to show Peter's window, too!

8. Music

Peter's father is in advertising and he has written a commercial for Juicy-O, a juice that tastes like oranges, pineapples, grapefruits, pears, and bananas. Pretend that you are in the advertising business. Write a jingle for a brand-new product that is going to hit the stores soon. You can rewrite the words to a familiar tune, write the music and the lyrics, or just write lyrics—rap-style!

9. Research

In chapter 4, Peter talks about a time when his father takes the family for a drive in the country to see the autumn leaves. The reds, yellows, and oranges seem extra brilliant to Peter, who has only seen leaves turn brown from the air pollution in the city. Research some areas in New England to which people might travel in the fall. Then create a travel brochure about one of these areas. Include interesting facts, scenic pictures or illustrations, and reasons to visit.

10. Math

Dribble, Peter's pet turtle, is one of his prized possessions. Peter wins Dribble at Jimmy Fargo's birthday party by estimating the number of jelly beans in a jar. Since his estimate of 348 is the closest to the actual number of 423, Peter wins. Peter knows that all the other boys are envious. Being able to estimate really paid off. Obtain a copy of page 43 from your teacher to give estimating a try.

11. Language Arts

In chapter 8, Fudge becomes a television star, but only after Peter helps persuade him to do it. Peter doesn't get to be in the commercial. He is just used to get Fudge to participate. In total frustration, Peter wonders how anyone would ever manage Fudge without him. Give Peter the reward he deserves by writing a TV commercial starring him! Make sure you advertise a product that Peter would like. Then perform your commercial for the class.

12. Social Studies

Peter and his friend Jimmy often play in nearby Central Park. On the day that Fudge decides he can fly, Peter, Jimmy, and Sheila are in the park when Mrs. Hatcher comes along with Fudge. Mrs. Hatcher leaves Fudge in the care of Sheila, who assures Mrs. Hatcher that she knows all about baby-sitting. Peter and Jimmy are supposed to help her. Sheila does not know nearly as much about baby-sitting as she thinks she does. Obtain a copy of page 44 from your teacher to create a guide for a child you might baby-sit, such as the child of a neighbor or family friend.

Hatcher Headquarters

Can you visualize where Peter lives based on the book, *Tales of a Fourth Grade Nothing*? Study the map of Manhattan below to help you get a clear picture of where Peter lives. Then use the map to answer the questions that follow.

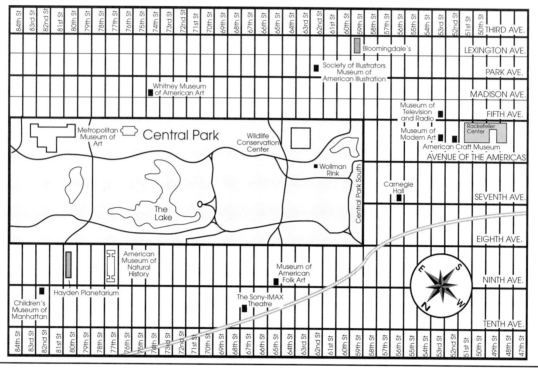

1. Locate the Hatchers' street, West 68th Street, and highlight it.

2. In which direction did Peter and Jimmy Fargo travel from Peter's apartment house to Central Park? Highlight Central Park. _____

3. The office of the Hatchers' dentist was located on the other side of the park, near Madison Avenue. Highlight Madison Ave. How many blocks east of Central Park is Madison Avenue? _____

4. What museum is located in Central Park? Highlight it. _____

5. Do you think Peter could walk from West 68th Street to the museum in Central Park? Why or why not? _____

6. According to this map, how many museums could Peter visit without going very far from home? Highlight them. _____

7. Mrs. Hatcher took the boys to Bloomingdale's® department store to buy shoes. Bloomingdale's is located at 3rd Avenue and 59th Street. Highlight a route from West 68th Street to Bloomingdale's. Then write the directions below using words like *left* and *right* or *north* and *south*. _____
_____
_____

8. If you could visit Manhattan, where would you want to visit the most? The least? _____
_____
_____

©2001 The Education Center, Inc. • *Contracts for Independent Readers • Humor* • TEC790 • Key p. 63

42   **Note to the teacher:** Use with activity #6 on page 40.

In My Estimation

Use your estimation skills to answer the following questions. Show your work on the back of this sheet.

1. Peter wins his turtle by estimating the number of jelly beans in the jar. If the top row across has about 38 jelly beans, and there are about 11 rows, how many jelly beans do you estimate are in the jar? _____

2. Mrs. Hatcher leaves Fudge in the park with Sheila, Peter, and Jimmy for a short time. If it takes her about 8 minutes to walk home from the park, and 3 minutes to go up to their apartment, estimate how long it will take her to go home and then return to the park. _____

3. Peter is studying New York City transportation. If it takes a bus 5 minutes to travel 9 city blocks, estimate how many city blocks the bus will travel in 15 minutes.

   _____

4. Peter's mom is surprised to see Fudge in a Toddle-Bike commercial on television. If Fudge's commercial appears twice a day during the month of May, about how many times will the commercial appear? _____

5. The elevator in Peter's building carries residents up and down every day. If the elevator makes 6 trips per hour, with 4 stops per trip, estimate how many stops the elevator makes between the hours of 8 A.M. and 11 A.M. _____

6. Peter, Fudge, and Mr. Hatcher go to the neighborhood theater to see *A Bear's Life*. If the admission price for one person is $4.95, estimate the cost of admission for 3 people. _____

7. After getting new shoes, Mrs. Hatcher takes Peter and Fudge to Hamburger Heaven for lunch. If Mrs. Hatcher has a $20.00 bill, and each meal costs $5.75, about how much change will she get back? _____

8. Peter and Jimmy work hard on their transportation poster, only to have to redo it. If each boy spent $4\frac{1}{2}$ hours making the first poster, estimate the total number of hours they will have put into the project once they have finished the second poster.

   _____

9. New York City has many taxis. If 8 taxis pass the movie theater every 5 minutes, about how many taxis will pass in one hour? _____

©2001 The Education Center, Inc. • *Contracts for Independent Readers* • Humor • TEC790 • Key p. 63

Note to the teacher: Use with activity #10 on page 41.

Name _____

Baby-Sitter's Guide

Cut out the boxes below and glue them onto index cards. Choose a child you might baby-sit and ask the child's parents to help you fill in the information in each space. Use the remaining index cards to create a front and back cover for your guide. On the back cover list any other important information, such as favorite games and favorite TV shows. Then punch two holes in the left-hand side and tie a piece of string in each hole to complete your guide.

Family Information

Parents' Names: _____

Child's Name and Age: _____
Home Address: _____
_____

Home Phone Number: _____
Special Information: _____
_____

Important Telephone Numbers

Emergency: _____
Doctor(s): _____
_____

Neighbors: _____
_____

Relatives: _____
_____

Food Tips

Allergies: _____
Snacks Allowed: _____
_____

Serving Amounts: _____
_____

Snacks Not Allowed: _____
_____

Safety Tips

Location of First-Aid Kit: _____
Do's and Don'ts: _____
_____
_____
_____

Note to the teacher: Use with activity #12 on page 41.

The Plant That Ate Dirty Socks
by Nancy McArthur

About the Book

Michael and Norman are stuck sharing a bedroom. Michael's layers of litter are always edging their way over the boundary line toward Norman's neat side, causing problems between the two. When Michael and Norman plant two mail-order bean seeds and they begin to grow, the problems grow faster than the plants. First, the family discovers that the plants have a special appetite for socks. Next, Mom and Dad begin making plans to get rid of the pesky plants. Then Michael begins making plans to save them. From the ultimate sacrifice of keeping a totally neat room to entering the sock-eating plants in the science fair, Michael gives his heart and soul to saving the plants.

About the Author

Nancy McArthur was born on October 30 in Cleveland, Ohio. She is one of three children, including a neat brother and a neat sister. Nancy was the messy one. Their home was always filled with books because her parents loved to read. When an aunt gave her a diary for her birthday, she began writing about her daily life. Then her father brought home an old typewriter and she began writing stories. By the time Nancy was 13, she had decided she wanted to have something published. Her first published writing was for her high school newspaper.

After graduating from Baldwin-Wallace College, McArthur had a few writing jobs, such as working in public relations, and writing magazine and newspaper articles. Then she began teaching journalism at Baldwin-Wallace College and writing books.

McArthur had an idea for *The Plant That Ate Dirty Socks* but filed it away. Later she thought about the kind of character that would want a plant that ate dirty socks. She decided it would be a messy kid. Since she was the messy kid in her family, she was able to draw from her own experiences, as well as her imagination, to write this funny story.

Student Contract Materials List

- Activity #1: construction paper, crayons or markers
- Activity #2: paper, pencil
- Activity #3: construction paper, crayons or markers
- Activity #4: 3 sheets of 8½" x 11" construction paper, arts-and-crafts supplies
- Activity #5: copy of page 48
- Activity #6: paper, pencil
- Activity #7: paper, pencil
- Activity #8: newspaper articles and letters to the editor, colored pencil
- Activity #9: white drawing paper, crayons or markers
- Activity #10: copy of page 49
- Activity #11: reference materials on houseplants, white drawing paper, crayons or markers
- Activity #12: reference materials on ventriloquism, puppet

45

The Plant That Ate Dirty Socks

Independent Contract

Name:_____ Number of activities to be completed: _____

 Language Arts

Michael's letter to the editor sparks the interest of a local television station. They want to conduct an interview with him about his unusual pet plant. Imagine that you have an unusual pet plant and a reporter from a local TV station wants to interview you. Write an interview between you and the reporter, giving the details about your plant's unusual abilities. Then draw a poster of your plant to have in the background as a friend asks the interview questions and you supply the answers for the class.

 Writing

The students in Norman's class are going to be writing letters to their local newspaper about issues they are either for or against. The paper publishes student letters weekly in the Saturday edition and Norman's teacher plans on sending theirs in for possible publication. Pretend that you are in Norman's class. What current issue do you feel strongly for or against? Write a letter for the Saturday edition of your local newspaper and submit it to your teacher for consideration.

 Art

What does your bedroom look like? Are you more a messy Michael or a neat Norman? Reread the first two pages of the book to remind yourself of their differences. Imagine sharing your room with a sibling who is your total opposite. Draw a picture of what your shared bedroom looks like, including a dividing line, such as tape, a curtain, or string. On the back write a list of room rules that you will both have to follow in order to be able to share the room in peace.

 Language Arts

All of Michael's friends are working on ideas for the science fair. Michael enters his plants and then has to wait until the judges award the prizes before he can take them home. Reread chapter 12 to find out what some of the students are doing for their projects. Then do some judging of your own. Create three medals—gold for first place, silver for second, and bronze for third. Award three of the experiments mentioned in the book with these medals. Then write a brief paragraph on the back of each medal explaining why each project deserves the award it receives.

 Science

All living things need certain ingredients to grow. Michael and Norman experiment with several items to see what will stimulate more growth in their two plants. In the end they discover that socks are the only things that keep their plants healthy. Obtain a copy of page 48 from your teacher to find out what all living things need in order to grow.

 Music

Norman not only talks to his plant, but sings to it as well. His favorite song is "Camptown Races," especially the "doo-dah, doo-dah" part, which he sings at the top of his voice. What type of music would you choose to sing to your plants? Slow or fast? Soft or loud? Rock or jazz? Compile a list of at least ten songs that you feel would make your plant grow faster. Then write a list of ten songs that you think would keep your plant from growing.

The Plant That Ate Dirty Socks

Independent Contract

Name:_____   Number of activities to be completed: _____

Critical Thinking

Jason is excited to know the secret of Norman and Michael's plants. His enthusiasm worries Michael, who decides they should use code words to prevent the secret from leaking out. The code is simple. Reread the beginning of chapter 10 to see how the code is used. Then create a word-substitution code with a friend. Write a letter to your friend using your secret code. Then copy the letter on a separate sheet of paper along with a key for your teacher.

Language Arts

Norman is surprised when his letter appears in the newspaper with parts left out. Then he remembers what his teacher said about editors sometimes shortening letters or articles when there is not enough room to print the entire piece. Look through several newspaper letters and articles that are at least 300 words in length. Choose one to edit down to 150 words or less. To do this, use a colored pencil to mark through any information you think is unnecessary. Then copy what is left onto a sheet of paper. Read over what you have written to make sure it makes sense and includes the author's main idea.

Art

Michael and Norman are opposites when it comes to the care of their room. Norman loves order and neatness. Michael is happy leaving everything on the floor. However, Michael does not like being nagged by Norman and his mom about his messy habits. Sometimes he dreams about inventing a robot to make his bed and clean his room. Design a robot that could do your unwanted chores. Make a drawing of your robot and write a brief description of what it can do.

Math

Norman and Michael plot and plan ways to convince their mom and dad to allow them to keep their unusual plants. One clever idea is to compare the care of plants to the care of animals. Obtain a copy of page 49 from your teacher to make your own comparisons.

Science

One of Mom's solutions to the growing plant problem is to take cuttings from the huge plants to grow smaller versions. Research houseplants to find out what types of plants can grow new plants from cuttings, such as begonias and geraniums. Then find out how they grow from cuttings into plants. Make a pamphlet with the information you find, complete with illustrations. You may wish to try out this new information and your own green thumb by taking a cutting of a plant and helping it grow.

Language Arts

Norman enjoys the challenge of trying to get his plant, Fluffy, to speak. But when Michael's friend Jason hears an "Ex," an "Ow," and a "Me" coming from Fluffy, Michael tries to convince Jason that Norman is a ventriloquist and is the real owner of the voice. Research ventriloquism, learn some of the techniques, and then practice speaking without moving your lips. Try to project your voice and speak clearly as you practice in front of a mirror. Obtain or make a puppet; then write a short dialogue between the two of you. Practice the script and then perform for your class.

The Key to Life

Stanley, Fluffy, people, and real plants all have one thing in common that they need in order to survive. Follow the trail to find this key to life.

Directions: Each phrase below describes a word. For each phrase, lightly shade the word that it is describing. If you make the correct choice, the trail will lead you to the key to life. The first one is done for you.

1. Stanley's favorite food	pizza	clean socks	dirty socks
2. 65 percent of the human body	salt	water	hair
3. used by plants during photosynthesis	socks	soil	sunlight
4. Fluffy's favorite food	dirty socks	clean socks	plant food
5. people need this for protection against the weather	shelter	oxygen	pancakes
6. dissolves the nutrients plants need	water	carbon dioxide	oxygen
7. plants need this so they don't get too hot or too cold	blankets	suitable climate	heater
8. how people get nutrients	shopping	skiing	eating
9. human waste that plants need	hair	carbon dioxide	dirt
10. Norman filled his blaster with this for Fluffy	syrup	water	juice

sunlight

water

socks

Research to find out why the trail led you to the item it did. Then, in the space provided, write a paragraph about the importance of this item to plants and people.

_____

_____

_____

_____

Note to the teacher: Use with activity #5 on page 46.

Best Pet for the Money

Michael and Norman are trying desperately to find a way to keep their plants. In chapter 5 Michael compares the price of cat food, dog food, and socks to find the cheapest one.

Directions: Read the price of the pet foods listed below and the amount each pet eats per day. Then complete the table to discover which pet is the cheapest to feed.

$1.29
per can

$0.89
per can

$5.28
per 6 pairs

$7.36
per 32 oz.

$8.00
per 32 oz.

Amount per Day:

small dog—1 can per day
sock-eating plant—¼ sock per day
guinea pig—1 oz. per day

cat—1 can per day
bird—1 oz. per day
large dog—2 cans per day

Pet	Cost per Day	Cost per Week (7 days)	Cost per Month (30 days)	Cost per Year (365 days)
small dog				
cat				
sock-eating plant				
bird				
guinea pig				
large dog				

1. Which pet is the cheapest to feed? _____

2. Do you think this was a good argument for Michael to use to keep their plants? Why or why not? _____

3. What other arguments could Michael and Norman use in order to keep their plants?

_____

_____

Ramona's World
by Beverly Cleary

About the Book

Fourth grade is going to be the best year ever for Ramona Quimby. At least the first day of school is perfect. Ramona has the biggest calluses on her hands, Yard Ape sits close to her, she has a new baby sister named Roberta, and she meets a new best friend named Daisy. Unfortunately, by the second day of school life returns to normal for Ramona. Her fourth-grade teacher, Mrs. Meacham, is a stickler for spelling. Roberta demands much of her mother's attention, especially when Ramona needs to talk. Even her friendship with Daisy is not perfect, as Ramona realizes when she accidentally crashes through the dining room ceiling at Daisy's house. Ramona discovers there are many challenges to conquer in the fourth grade!

About the Author

Beverly Cleary was born on April 12, 1916, in McMinnville, Oregon. After earning two bachelor's degrees, one in librarianship, she became a children's librarian. She began writing children's books in 1950 with the introduction of *Henry Huggins*. Her work is highly praised for its honest portrayal of children. She has the rare ability and talent to recreate the daily ups and downs of childhood with great empathy. She has earned numerous writing awards, including the 1984 Newbery Medal for *Dear Mr. Henshaw*.

Interestingly, when Beverly Cleary first attended school she regarded reading traditional children's books as boring. It wasn't until she was in the third grade that she experienced the joy of reading for pleasure and became a frequent visitor to the public library. She wanted to read funny stories with characters that were similar to her childhood friends. That's when she began to consider a future career as a children's writer. Cleary once stated, "Childhood is universal, and I write about feelings as I knew them growing up."

Student Contract Materials List

- Activity #1: copy of page 53
- Activity #2: reference book with a Food Guide Pyramid, crayons or markers
- Activity #3: notebook, dictionary
- Activity #4: drawing paper, art supplies
- Activity #5: paper, pencil
- Activity #6: shoebox, arts-and-crafts supplies
- Activity #7: paper, pencil
- Activity #8: half sheet of poster board, art supplies
- Activity #9: blank tape, tape recorder
- Activity #10: copy of page 54
- Activity #11: crayons or markers
- Activity #12: white construction paper, art supplies

Ramona's World

Independent Contract

Name: _____   Number of activities to be completed: _____

 1. **Language Arts**

Ramona's least favorite subject in school is spelling. She becomes upset when Mrs. Meacham uses some of her misspelled words as examples of poor spelling. Ramona doesn't understand what difference spelling makes if people know what she means to say. Mrs. Meacham responds with an example from a sentence that Ramona has written in which she misuses the word *coach* in place of the word *couch*. Reread chapter 2 and then obtain a copy of page 53 from your teacher. Complete the sheet to see that spelling really does matter.

 2. **Science**

On the first day of school Ramona shares part of her lunch with her new friend Daisy. Discover what is needed to pack the perfect lunch. First, research the Food Guide Pyramid; then plan a healthy lunch with foods from each section. Next, draw and label a Food Guide Pyramid on paper. In the correct sections on the pyramid, draw pictures of the foods you've chosen to pack for lunch. Later, use your pyramid to compare to a friend's lunch to determine if he or she is eating foods from each section.

 3. **Language Arts**

In chapter 7 Ramona has a reflective moment as she thinks about the world of words. She feels incompetent as a speller and seems to be surrounded by words; everywhere she looks there are words! Take time to discover the words around your world. For one day, notice words on billboards, in stores, on traffic signs, etc. Keep a notebook with you to write down as many words as possible and note where each is located. Then check the spelling of each word. Later, review your findings to determine which area of your world has the most words.

 4. **Art**

Ramona is pleased to report to Mrs. Meacham that she has seen a license plate with the misspelled word *LIBARY* on it. Mrs. Meacham congratulates Ramona for noticing the misspelling. She informs Ramona that the owner of the plate is probably an excellent speller, but a personalized license plate is limited to six letters. Design and illustrate a personalized license plate using only six letters. Create your own message, such as CUSOON (see you soon), and then write a description of its meaning on the back of the plate.

 5. **Writing**

In chapter 10 Ramona is concerned about finding the right valentine for her secret sweetheart, Yard Ape. She thinks boxed valentines are too silly, and a poem seems icky-sweet. She decides to give him a picture of herself with no message. Yard Ape writes Ramona an original poem. When she reads it she smiles. Write three original valentine poems: one for a boy, one for a girl, and one for a teacher. Then watch for smiles all around.

 6. **Art**

Ramona and Daisy have a great time playing together until they get carried away with the princess-and-witch game. Daisy believes the attic is the perfect dungeon for the princess. She never considers that Ramona may crash through the dining room ceiling. Read chapter 5 and then recreate the scene in a diorama, with Princess Ramona stuck in the ceiling.

Ramona's World
Independent Contract

Name: _____ Number of activities to be completed: _____

7. Writing

In chapter 5 when Ramona tells her family about the frightening experience she has endured at Daisy's house, she exaggerates the tale, making it sound worse than it really is. Write your own exaggerated story. Describe a new best friend, her family, her house, and the wacky time the two of you have together one afternoon.

8. Social Studies

Ramona desperately wants a best friend, and she finds one in Daisy. Make a list of the characteristics that you would like a best friend to have. Create a pie chart to represent those characteristics. Draw a large circle in the center of a half sheet of poster board. Then decide how important each characteristic is to you. If a characteristic is very important, give it a large pie piece. If it is less important, give it a smaller pie piece. Label each section with the corresponding characteristic. Finish the pie chart by drawing an illustration for each one. Title your poster and then share it with the class.

9. Social Studies

Ramona loves both of her sisters, but sometimes she wishes her family didn't have so many girls. Whether you are the first, last, middle, or only child, experiencing positive and negative feelings about family is normal. Interview four people: a first, a last, a middle, and an only child. Ask each one what he likes and what he dislikes about his position in the family as you tape-record the responses. Summarize your findings and then determine whether there are any similarities among the four groups.

10. Language Arts

Ramona's mom cautions her about using the word *stuff* frequently. She urges Ramona to think of a better word to express herself. Ramona thinks *stuff* is a good word choice; it is convenient, it has multiple meanings, and it is easy to spell. However, this kind of all-purpose word can cause mixed-up communications. Obtain a copy of page 54 from your teacher to explore how an all-purpose word can cause confusion.

11. Writing

On the first day of school, Mrs. Meacham instructs her students to write a paragraph about themselves. Ramona enjoys writing and has plenty to say about herself. Write a descriptive paragraph about yourself, including four things that no one else in your class knows about you. Then draw a picture to illustrate your paragraph.

12. Science

Ramona loves to watch *Big Hospital* on television. It is a way for her to forget her troubles, like not being a good speller. To be healthy everyone needs to take time to relax, but watching television may not always be the best choice. Brainstorm a list of healthy ways to relax after school, such as exercising or playing sports. Then create a brochure including your ideas and information on how classmates can follow your suggestions. Illustrate your brochure with pictures that will make your readers excited about relaxing in a healthy way.

Spelling Matters

In the example below, the sentences are funny because they show the confusion that can result when words are misspelled. Follow the example to write a funny sentence for each word listed. Then choose one sentence to copy and illustrate on a separate sheet of paper.

Example: couch/coach The couch directed the team's warm-up exercises.
I was so tired after soccer practice that I took a nap on the coach!

1. power/powder
   _____
   _____

2. fiend/friend
   _____
   _____

3. decrease/decease
   _____
   _____

4. from/form
   _____
   _____

5. dessert/desert
   _____
   _____

6. wart/war
   _____
   _____

7. spill/spell
   _____
   _____

8. hose/nose
   _____
   _____

9. bad/bed
   _____
   _____

10. sign/sing
    _____
    _____

Note to the teacher: Use with activity #1 on page 51.

Mixed-Up Messages

A. Write what you think Ramona means for each sentence below. Then write what you believe Ramona's mom might think she means. Finally, write your prediction for the result of the mixed-up message. The first one is done for you.

1. Ramona says, "I need some stuff to wear to school."
   She means: *She needs her costume for the class play.*
   Mom might think: *Ramona needs clean gym clothes.*
   The result: *Ramona will have to wear her gym clothes for the class play.*

2. Ramona says, "Mrs. Meacham wants me to bring some stuff for the Valentine's Day Party!"
   She means: _____
   Mom might think: _____
   The result: _____

3. Ramona says, "I want to do fun stuff at my birthday party."
   She means: _____
   Mom might think: _____
   The result: _____

4. Ramona says, "I can do stuff with Roberta."
   She means: _____
   Mom might think: _____
   The result: _____

5. Ramona says, "Please get me some good stuff for my birthday."
   She means: _____
   Mom might think: _____
   The result: _____

6. Ramona says, "Daisy and I want some stuff to eat."
   She means: _____
   Mom might think: _____
   The result: _____

B. Use the words in the box to write a paragraph in the space provided. On the back of this page, rewrite your paragraph, replacing the words from the box with words that better express your meaning. Ask a friend to read your first paragraph and then explain what he thinks it means. Then share your rewritten paragraph with your friend and discuss any mixed-up messages.

Word Box
stuff
thing
junk
cool
dude
whatever

_____
_____
_____
_____
_____
_____

©2001 The Education Center, Inc. • *Contracts for Independent Readers* • Humor • TEC790

54   **Note to the teacher:** Use with activity #10 on page 52.

Boy: Tales of Childhood
by Roald Dahl

About the Book

Roald Dahl shares some of his most memorable boyhood stories in *Boy: Tales of Childhood.* Since all the stories are true, the insights from these pages certainly give the reader a fair overview of who Roald Dahl was and why he wrote the way he did.

There are some funny accounts, such as the Great Mouse Plot in which he and some fellow classmates learn the consequences of sweet revenge when they enter mean Mrs. Pratchett's sweet-shop and sneak a dead mouse into a jar of Gobstoppers. There are also some terrifying stories, such as the one about his first automobile ride in which he nearly loses his nose. Expect the unexpected in this hilarious account of Roald Dahl's boyhood.

About the Author

Roald Dahl was born on September 13, 1916, in Llandaff, South Wales. Dahl was a fun-loving, mischievous child. His father died when he was four. Dahl attended Llandaff Cathedral School, then boarding school at St. Peter's, and finally a well-known private school, Repton. Dahl was never a superior student. He was a natural athlete, but was not considered a leader.

After his schooling, Dahl chose to work for the Shell Oil Company in Africa rather than go on to college. In 1939, he joined the Royal Air Force, serving first as a pilot in Africa, and later as an assistant air attaché in Washington, D.C. During this time, he was interviewed by the *Saturday Evening Post*. The interviewer didn't take notes, so he picked up the notes Dahl took for him. Finding that these were actually a story, the reporter sent them to the magazine under Dahl's name. Dahl later stated that becoming a writer was a complete fluke. His first children's book was called *The Gremlins*. Later, Dahl made up bedtime stories for his five children, learning from them what children like. He kept their interest by throwing in unexpected twists. This technique is characteristic of Roald Dahl, one of the best-known authors of humorous books for children.

Student Contract Materials List

- Activity #1: paper, pencil
- Activity #2: paper, pencil
- Activity #3: construction paper, crayons or markers
- Activity #4: 8½" x 11" poster board, white drawing paper, scissors, crayons or markers
- Activity #5: copy of page 58, 1 sheet of 12" x 18" construction paper, scissors, glue, crayons or markers
- Activity #6: white drawing paper, crayons or markers

- Activity #7: cardboard box, arts-and-crafts supplies
- Activity #8: paper, pencil
- Activity #9: reference materials on penicillin, experiment materials
- Activity #10: reference materials on artists, art supplies, index card
- Activity #11: copy of page 59
- Activity #12: copy of page 60

Boy: Tales of Childhood

Independent Contract

Name: _____ Number of activities to be completed: _____

 1. **Language Arts**

At the beginning of *Boy,* Roald Dahl includes a note to the reader explaining that this book is a collection of stories taken from the events of his own life. He says that these are not important events; they are the things that for some reason have been seared on his memory. What events in your life are forever seared into your memory? Write a descriptive story about an unforgettable experience that you have had. Then illustrate your story.

 2. **Writing**

Roald begins writing weekly letters to his mother when he is only nine years old because on Sunday mornings every boy at St. Peter's is required to do so. Strict supervision limits the content of their letters, but Roald's mother saves every letter he writes to her. Pretend you are one of Roald's classmates and are allowed an opportunity to write home totally unsupervised. What stories would you tell about your funny classmate Roald? Write a letter to your mother in which you highlight some of Roald's fun and crazy antics.

 3. **Art**

In "The Bicycle and the Sweet-Shop," Roald Dahl details the glorious candies he loves so much in Mrs. Pratchett's sweet-shop. Reread this section, in which he describes everything from Bull's-eyes and Glacier Mints to Liquorice Bootlaces and Gobstoppers. Then draw what you imagine the candy counter in the sweet-shop looks like filled with all the colorful, mouthwatering candies. Be sure to draw a sign next to each candy telling what it is.

 4. **Art**

Uniforms are required in the schools Roald attends. He describes in detail the two different uniforms he has to wear in "First Day" and "Getting Dressed for the Big School." Think about the type of uniform you would want to wear if you had to wear one. Draw and cut out a boy and a girl paper doll. Then design, color, and cut out two uniforms for each paper doll, one for winter and one for summer. Share your paper dolls with the class, explaining why you chose the uniform styles and whether you think uniforms are a good idea for school.

 5. **Social Studies**

In the opening chapter of *Boy,* Roald Dahl shares some of his family ancestry as he introduces the reader to his grandfather, father, and uncle through some of their stories. From 1820, when his grandfather was born, to 1984, when Roald Dahl wrote the book, many important events occurred, some of which he shares in the book. A fun way to organize a family history is to make a timeline that highlights some of the important events in the family. Obtain a copy of page 58 from your teacher and make a timeline of your own.

 6. **Language Arts**

Every summer Mrs. Dahl packs up her large family and travels from England to Norway for a vacation on the island of Tjöme. Roald calls this "The Magic Island." Create a travel brochure to advertise this island as the perfect spot for a family's summer vacation. Reread the chapter "The Magic Island" to refresh your memory. Focus on the details that would compel your classmates to choose this beautiful location for their next family vacation. Use illustrations to really sell the island.

Sherbet Sucker

Tickler
Tickler

Boy: Tales of Childhood

Independent Contract

Name:_____ Number of activities to be completed: _____

7. | Art

According to Roald, every boy who goes to an English preparatory school takes a tuck-box with him. Inside a tuck-box a boy stashes all of his treasures and the weekly goodies his mother sends from home. Reread the first few pages of "First Day" about Roald's treasures. Think about what you would pack in a tuck-box of your own. Then make a tuck-box by decorating a box and placing the things inside that you would want to take with you if you went away to school.

8. | Writing

In the chapter "Captain Hardcastle," Roald cannot finish his writing assignment "The Life Story of a Penny" because he has broken the nib of his pen. He is scared to ask Captain Hardcastle for a nib, so he can't finish his story. Think about what Roald might have been thinking. Then write your own story titled "The Life Story of a Penny."

9. | Science

When Roald's oldest sister dies from appendicitis and his father dies from pneumonia, there are no miraculous antibiotics available to help fight off the bacteria that caused these illnesses. Penicillin was not even discovered until 1928, eight years after these two deaths. Research the discovery of penicillin by Sir Alexander Fleming. How did he accidentally discover it? Devise a simple experiment in which you grow mold and use it as a focal point in a presentation to the class about the miracle antibiotic, penicillin.

10. | Art

One of Roald's great interests as an older boy is photography. Through his talent in this area, he becomes friends with Arthur Norris, an art teacher. Norris spends time talking to Roald about the great artists and sharing his love of art. Choose a famous artist, sculptor, photographer, or painter. Research to find out about this person's life and work. Then create a piece of art in the same style as this artist. On an index card, write the title of your piece and a few facts about the artist whose style you copied.

11. | Science

The boys in Roald's school have the great fortune to occasionally get to sample Cadbury® chocolates. The boys are part of the testing process for new products. This experience causes Roald's imagination to explore the development of candy by the chocolate company. Use your imagination to help you invent a new candy bar. Then obtain a copy of page 59 from your teacher to develop your new candy bar idea!

12. | Social Studies

In the 1920s and 1930s, Roald lives in South Wales and England. His family spends their summers in Norway, where his grandparents live. He attends boarding schools in Weston-super-Mare and Derby. Obtain a copy of page 60 from your teacher to learn where these places are.

Timeline of Mine

Roald Dahl wrote *Boy: Tales of Childhood* in order to share some memorable events in his life. Another way to share memorable events is with a timeline. Create a timeline of interesting events in your life by following the directions below.

Directions:

1. Pick a date with which to begin your timeline. This can be your birth, your first memory, or an event that someone has told you about but you don't remember.

2. Interview family members or friends to help you remember the details of nine other important events in your life.

3. In each of the boxes below write the date and a brief explanation of the event that occurred on that date.

4. Cut out each box.

5. On a sheet of construction paper, draw a timeline with ten places to glue the boxes, alternating placement on top and bottom to allow for more room.

6. Glue each box onto the timeline in its proper order.

7. Below or above each box, on the opposite side of the timeline, draw an illustration of each event.

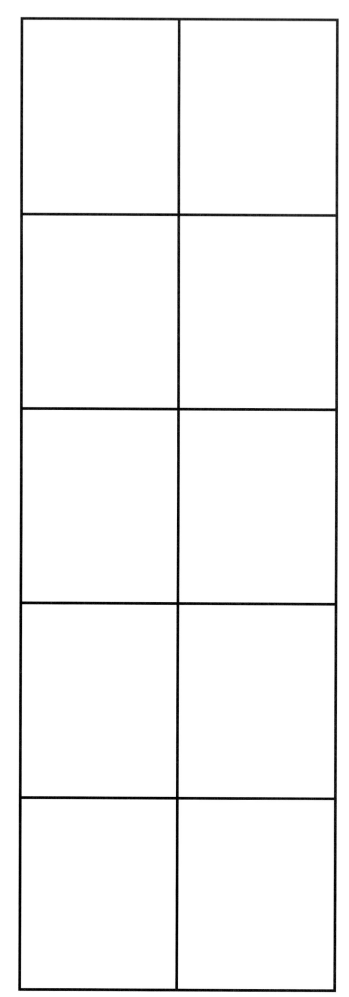

Note to the teacher: Use with activity #5 on page 56.

Latest Invention: The New Candy Bar

You have been assigned the task of creating a new and delicious candy bar for kids everywhere. Fill in the spaces below to develop your new candy bar.

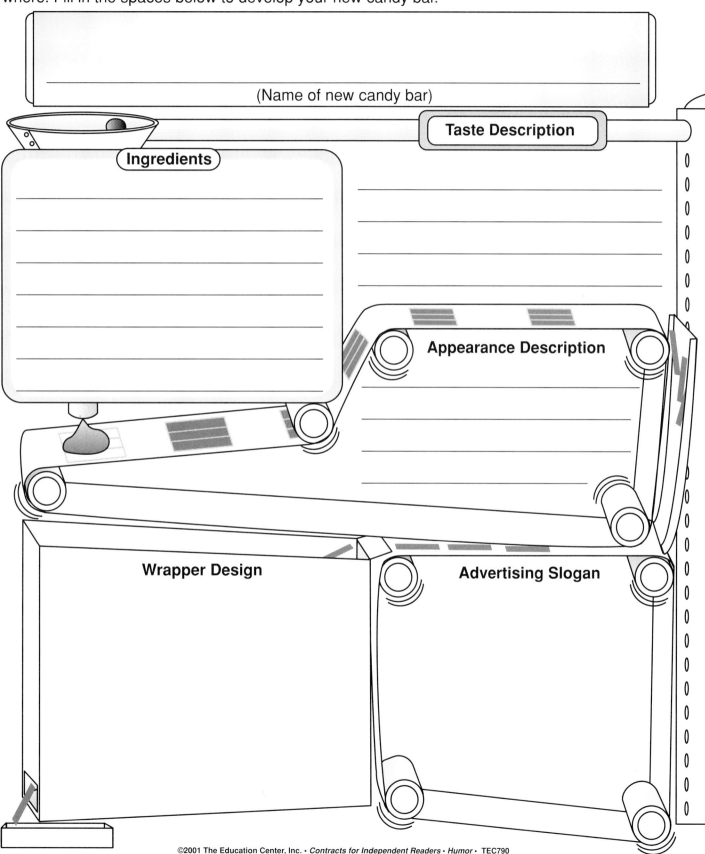

(Name of new candy bar)

Taste Description

Ingredients

Appearance Description

Wrapper Design

Advertising Slogan

©2001 The Education Center, Inc. • *Contracts for Independent Readers* • *Humor* • TEC790

A Boy and His Home

Find the locations where Roald Dahl grew up, went to school, and went on vacation.

Directions: Study the map below. Highlight each of the following locations: Llandaff, South Wales; Cardiff, South Wales; Weston-super-Mare, England; Derby, England; London, England; Newcastle, England; Oslo, Norway; and Tjöme, Norway. Then answer the questions that follow.

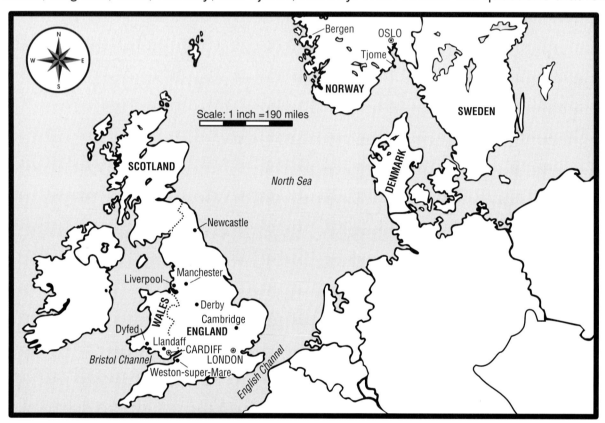

1. Llandaff, South Wales, is the birthplace of Roald Dahl. What large city is it near?

   _____

2. Weston-super-Mare is where Roald attended St. Peter's School. What body of water separates Weston-super-Mare from Cardiff? _____

3. Repton School is near Derby, England. What direction is Derby from London? _____

4. The Dahl family took a five-hour train trip from London to Newcastle. About how many miles is it from London to Newcastle? _____

5. From Newcastle, the family took a boat trip to Oslo, Norway, lasting two days and one night. About how many miles is it from Newcastle, England, to Oslo, Norway?

   _____

6. From Oslo, in which direction did they travel to reach their final destination of Tjöme?

   _____

Books to Tickle Your Funny Bone

Laugh, chuckle, snort, giggle,
and smile ear to ear with this collection of humorous novels.

Beetles, Lightly Toasted by Phyllis Reynolds Naylor • Andy wants to enter an imaginative writing contest so that he can finally get his name in the local paper. But when he finds out that the topic is conservation, he decides to boycott the contest.

The BFG by Roald Dahl • When Sophie is snatched out of the orphanage window in the middle of the night by a giant, she is relieved to find out that he is a big friendly giant. Now, she and the BFG must join hands to save humans from being gobbled up by the unfriendly, disgusting giants.

Chocolate Fever by Robert Kimmel Smith • Henry Green loves chocolate. He loves chocolate so much that he eats it for breakfast, lunch, snacks, and dinner. One day Henry breaks out in a chocolate-scented rash. Now he has to think about giving chocolate up for good!

The Exiles by Hilary McKay • Being sent to Big Grandma's house for the summer isn't the worst thing that could have happened to the Conroy sisters. Or maybe it is. They are expected to do chores and eat everything on their plates at mealtime, and they aren't allowed to read all day.

Frindle by Andrew Clements • Is the pen really mightier than the sword? How about a frindle? Nick Allen has invented a new word and he's getting everybody to use it, but Mrs. Granger, his fifth-grade teacher, is punishing anyone who says it in front of her. Who will win the battle over the word *frindle?*

The Great Brain by John D. Fitzgerald • J. D. really admires his older brother Tom, aka The Great Brain. Tom is always thinking of ways to make money. Sometimes J. D. prospers from this and sometimes he doesn't. What will Tom think of next and will J. D. come out ahead for a change?

Lizzie Logan Gets Married by Eileen Spinelli • Heather has all kinds of trouble, such as toaditus and chiropterophobia, that only her friend Lizzie Logan can help her with. With all of Lizzie's wedding plans, will she have time to help her best friend?

Otherwise Known as Sheila the Great by Judy Blume • Sheila is spending the summer in someone else's house in a small town instead of going to Disneyland®. She also has to take swimming lessons and live with a dog—her two worst fears. How will she ever survive the summer?

Skinnybones by Barbara Park • Alex Frankovitch is known for making people laugh. When he can't think of a true funny story, he makes one up. His stories could get him into a lot of trouble with his fifth-grade teacher and with a boy in his class whose brother is a major league baseball player.

Top Secret by John Reynolds Gardiner • Human photosynthesis? Is that possible? Nobody thinks so, except Allen Brewster and the president of the United States. How will Allen convince his friends, his teachers, and his parents that his turning green and sprouting roots isn't a practical joke?

Tut, Tut (The Time Warp Trio series) by Jon Scieszka • The Time Warp Trio has done it again. Just when they thought they wouldn't be swept away into another disaster, Joe's sister opens *The Book* and they are off. This time they go to Egypt to outsmart an evil high priest and rescue Joe's sister.

Wayside School Gets a Little Stranger by Louis Sachar • Wayside School has been closed for 243 days. The 30-story building with one room on each floor and no elevator is now open again! The students are excited, but they have no idea of the adventures that await them!

Answer Keys

Page 8

1. sardine sandwich
   peanut butter sandwich
   bologna sandwich
   a pear
   an orange
   a slice of strawberry-rhubarb pie
   a banana
   4 pieces of butter crumb cake
   an apple
   3 oatmeal raisin cookies
   2 helpings of cherry vanilla ice cream with chocolate fudge sauce

2. Students' answers will vary. Accept all reasonable responses.

3. **Milo's Servings**
   Fats: 2 ice creams, fudge sauce, pie, 3 cookies, 4 pieces of cake
   Dairy: 2 ice creams
   Meat, Poultry, Fish, Nuts: sardines, bologna, peanut butter
   Fruits: orange, banana, apple, pear, strawberries
   Grains: 6 slices of bread

   My Servings
   Students' answers will vary, but should correspond to the Food Guide Pyramid.

4. No, he should have had some vegetables and he shouldn't have eaten so many fats.

5. Students' responses will vary. Accept all reasonable responses.

Page 9

I. Student responses will vary. Accept all reasonable responses.
1. I didn't say a word.
2. I'm depending on you.
3. The person who doesn't procrastinate will get better things.
4. Please help me.
5. Don't expect something to happen before it does.
6. Words are more powerful than weapons.
7. People always think things are better somewhere else.
8. If something describes you, admit it.
9. Time can be spent or wasted, just like money.

Page 14

Page 15

1. MY DAILY PANIC FIT
2. COME RULE SCHOOL!
3. Answers will vary.
4. Answers will vary.

Page 16

1. H
2. A
3. R
4. I
5. U
6. C
7. E
8. L
9. D
10. N

L U N C H   A N D   D I N N E R

Page 20

I. Colors: Amber Brown, Kelly Green
   Rhymes: Bill Hill, Otto Donato
   Animals: Joey Roo, Kitty Katz
   Plants: Ivy Vine, Heather Branch
   Food: Melba Toast, Candy Apple
   Months: April Shower, August Heat
   Seasons: Summer Sun, Autumn Breeze
   Landscapes: Rocky Mountain, Sandy Beach

II. Students' responses will vary. Accept all reasonable responses.

III. Students' poems will vary.

Page 21

I.

II. A. New Jersey
    B. New York
    C. Walla Walla, Washington
    D. Paris
    E. London

III. Illustrations will vary.

Page 25

1. $3.33
2. $66.60
3. $99.90
4. $3.87
5. $1.92
6. $63.00
7. $75.00
8. Students' responses will vary. Accept all reasonable responses.
9. Students' responses will vary. Accept all reasonable responses.

page 26

	Team #1: Alan and Joe	Points	Team #2: Billy and Tom	Points
1.	Want to dig in the manure to pick the first worm.	0	Protest, so Alan and Joe let Tom pick the spot to dig the worm.	1
2.	Pick out a huge night crawler.	1	Check the dictionary for clarification.	0
3.	Tell a dramatic story to scare Billy.	0	Don't believe the story.	1
4.	Try to impose a time limit.	0	Beat the time limit.	1
5.	Glue two worms together.	0	Discover the trick.	1
6.	Tell Billy's mom.	0	Mom develops worm recipes.	1
7.	Take Billy to Shea Stadium and then bring him home late.	0	Billy wakes up just in time to find a worm to eat.	1
8.	Send a phony letter from Dr. McGrath.	0	Dad tells them it is a fake letter.	1
9.	Make a worm with beans.	0	Billy discovers the trick.	1
10.	Lock Billy inside a closet.	0	Dad lets him out.	1
11.	Plan to lower Billy into the cistern.	0	Dad stops them.	1
	Total	1	Total	10

Answers to student-written strategies and counterstrategies will vary; accept all reasonable responses.

Page 30

Pet	Number of babies per litter	Number of litters per year	Lowest number of babies per year	Highest number of babies per year
1. gopher	3–6	1	3	6
2. rat	6–12	3–6	18	72
3. pigeon	2	5–11	10	22
4. garter snake	7–85	1	7	85
5. dog	2–12	2	4	24
6. rabbit	4–5	1–5	4	25
7. owl	2–3	1	2	3
		Totals	48	237

8. the lowest: 72; the highest: 288
9. the lowest: 50; the highest: 110
10. the lowest: 4; the highest: 175

Page 31

1. Pacific Ocean
2. Alberta, Manitoba
3. Montana and North Dakota
4. about 1,400 miles; about 2,200 kilometers
5. 1,100; 1,700
6. south
7. Regina
8. about 1,750 miles

Page 32

Students' responses will vary. Possible responses are listed below.

1. B; Billy would not see a thousand ducks in a theater aisle.
2. A; Billy could not ride a canoe on a prairie.
3. A; Mr. Miller could not hide in a window shade.
4. A; Politicians would probably not toss bird nests out of trees.
5. A; The arrival of a dead skunk during dinner would not be a time of joy and peace.
6. B; Mules are not considered by most to be attractive.
7. B; Billy and his pets would not travel in a cardboard box.
8. A; The field looked like it had measles, so the spots are on the ground, not on the gophers.

Page 37

	Title	Character
1.	The Lion, the Witch, and the Wardrobe	White Witch
2.	The Tale of Peter Rabbit	Mr. McGregor
3.	Robin Hood	Sheriff of Nottingham
4.	The Legend of Sleepy Hollow	Headless Horseman
5.	Matilda	The Trunchbull
6.	Moby Dick	Captain Ahab
7.	Treasure Island	Long John Silver
8.	Alice in Wonderland	Red Queen
9.	The House at Pooh Corner	Eeyore
10.	The Hoboken Chicken Emergency	Henrietta
11.	Adventures of Tom Sawyer	Injun Joe
12.	Gods, Heroes, and Men of Ancient Greece	Cyclops

Page 38

1. drafting
2. toe-flicking
3. scissor
4. crossover
5. cadence
6. fakie
7. glide
8. stride

Pictures will vary.

Page 42

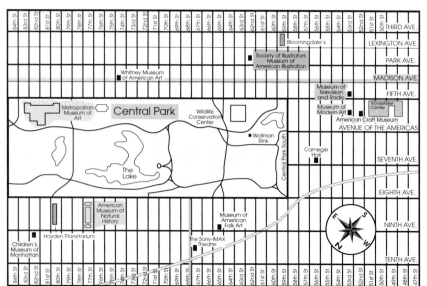

2. southeast
3. one
4. Metropolitan Museum of Art
5. Yes. Students' reasons will vary.
6. nine
7. Students' responses will vary.
   Accept all reasonable responses.
8. Students' responses will vary.
   Accept all reasonable responses.

Page 43

1. about 400 jellybeans
2. about 20 minutes
3. about 30 blocks
4. about 60 times
5. about 70 stops
6. about $15.00
7. about $2.00
8. about 20 hours
9. about 120 taxis

Page 48

pizza	clean socks	dirty socks
salt	water	hair
socks	soil	sunlight
dirty socks	clean socks	plant food
shelter	oxygen	pancakes
water	carbon dioxide	oxygen
blankets	suitable climate	heater
shopping	skiing	eating
hair	carbon dioxide	dirt
syrup	water	juice

Students' responses to the paragraph will vary, but should include the importance of water. Accept all reasonable responses.

Page 49

Pet	Cost per Day	Cost per Week (7 days)	Cost per Month (30 days)	Cost per Year (365 days)
small dog	$1.29	$9.03	$38.70	$470.85
cat	$0.89	$6.23	$26.70	$324.85
sock-eating plant	$0.22	$1.54	$6.60	$80.30
bird	$0.23	$1.61	$6.90	$83.95
guinea pig	$0.25	$1.75	$7.50	$91.25
large dog	$2.58	$18.06	$77.40	$941.70

1. sock-eating plant
2. Yes. Students' responses will vary. Accept all reasonable responses.
3. Students' responses will vary. Accept all reasonable responses.

Page 60

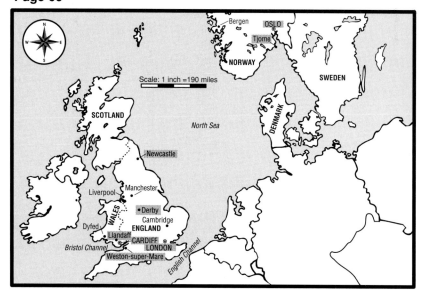

1. Cardiff
2. Bristol Channel
3. northwest
4. about 240 miles
5. about 570 miles
6. south